Ready-Made Centers
for Differentiated Instruction

Grade 5

Scott Foresman·Addison Wesley

enVisionMATH®
Common Core

PEARSON

Glenview, Illinois • Boston, Massachusetts • Chandler, Arizona • Upper Saddle River, New Jersey

ISBN-13: 978-0-328-71168-0
ISBN-10: 0-328-71168-3

1 2 3 4 5 6 7 8 9 V0FL 15 14 13 12 11

Common Core

Standards for Mathematical Content

Domain: Number and Operations in Base Ten
Topics: 1, 2, 3, 4, 5, 6, and 7

Domain: Operations and Algebraic Thinking
Topic: 8

Domain: Number and Operations—Fractions
Topics: 9, 10, and 11

Domain: Measurement and Data
Topics: 12, 13, and 14

Domain: Geometry
Topics: 15 and 16

Standards for Mathematical Practice

- ✔ Make sense of problems and persevere in solving them.
- ✔ Reason abstractly and quantitatively.
- ✔ Construct viable arguments and critique the reasoning of others.
- ✔ Model with mathematics.
- ✔ Use appropriate tools strategically.
- ✔ Attend to precision.
- ✔ Look for and make use of structure.
- ✔ Look for and express regularity in repeated reasoning.

Materials

1. Each of the 5 spiral-bound books in the box contains an on-level, one-star activity, and an advanced-level, two-star activity, for every lesson.

One-star activity

Two-star activity

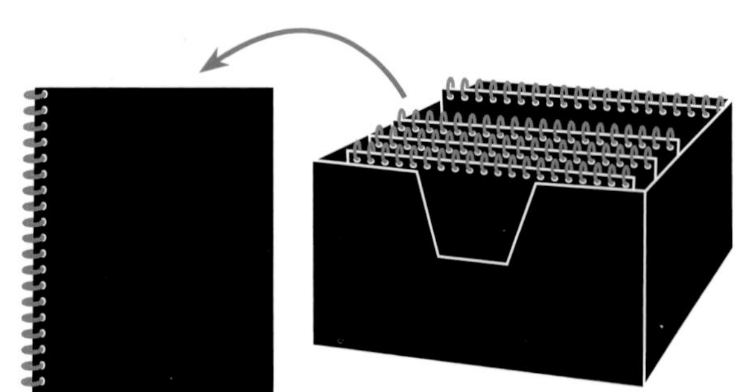

2. Manipulatives

40 number cubes

200 red and 200 blue square tiles

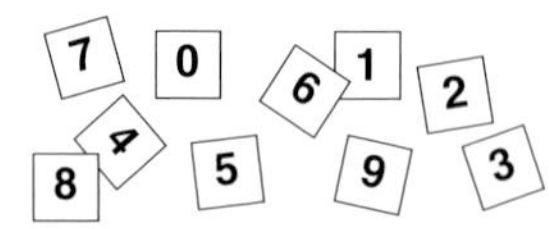

20 sets of number tiles (0-9)

3. Plastic Bags:

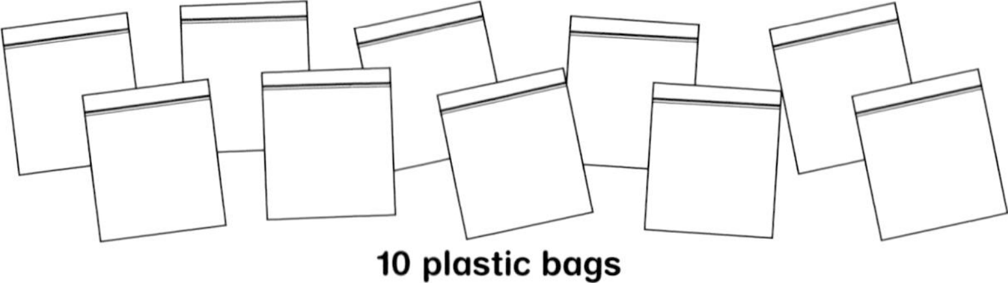
10 plastic bags

4. School-supplied items:

40 large paper clips

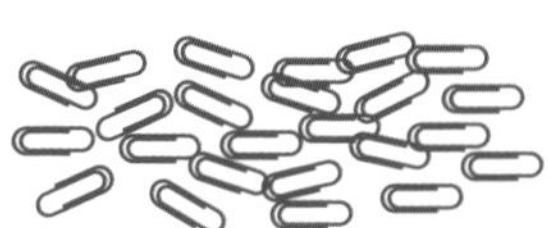
70 small paper clips

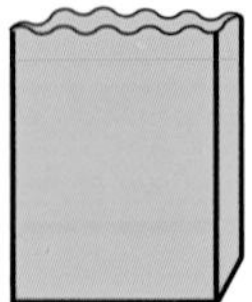
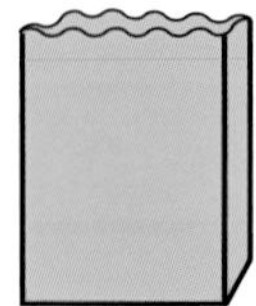
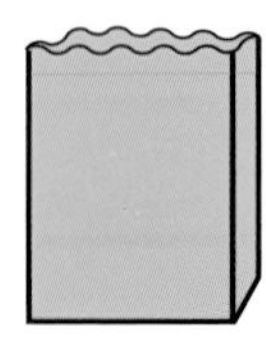
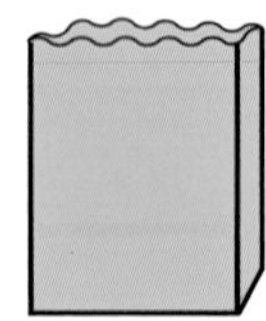
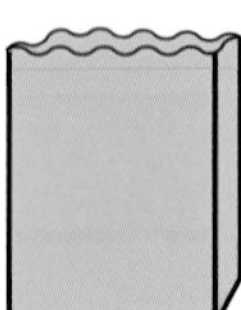
5 paper lunch bags

Setting Up

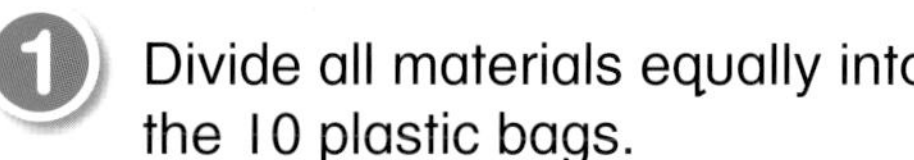

1. Divide all materials equally into the 10 plastic bags.

20 red square tiles

20 blue square tiles

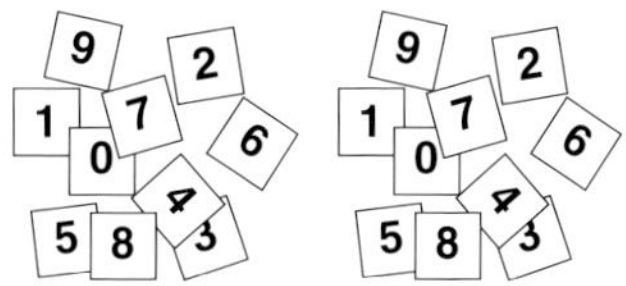

2 sets of number tiles (0-9)

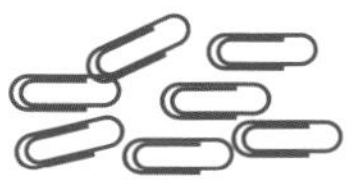

7 small paper clips

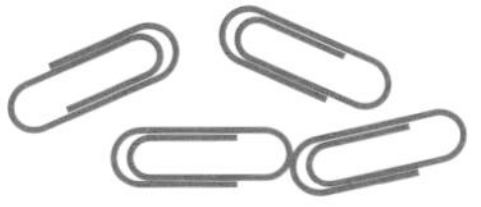

4 large paper clips

4 number cubes

2. Store the activity materials in the front section of the box.

"Grab and Go"

- Each group of students doing an activity grabs a book, a plastic bag of manipulatives, and (if needed) a paper bag. Groups then work independently to complete one or both leveled activities. Some activities in Grades 3 – 6 will require groups to grab two plastic bags of manipulatives.
- Occasionally, manipulatives and/or Teaching Tool masters used during the lesson will also be needed to complete the Center Activities.
- When students complete an activity, they return the book and the bag of manipulatives to the box.

Get Started 

Get 10 squares in one color and 10 in another color.
Get two number cubes. Take turns with another player or team.
Talk about math as you play!

At Your Turn

Toss two number cubes. Add the dots. Find your toss below.
Follow the directions. Explain your thinking. Cover the answer.
If the answer is taken, lose your turn. Have fun!

Toss	Read the value of each period. Find the number in standard form. Explain.
2	74 billion
3	407 billion
4	740 million
5	74 billion, 400 million
6	4 billion, 707 million
7	4 billion, 7 million
8	4 billion, 70 million
9	7 billion, 47 million
10	4 billion, 700 million
11	470 billion
12	47 billion

74,400,000,000	74,000,000,000	4,070,000,000	4,707,000,000
47,000,000,000	7,047,000,000	470,000,000,000	4,700,000,000
4,707,000,000	4,007,000,000	407,000,000,000	7,047,000,000
4,070,000,000	740,000,000	74,400,000,000	4,007,000,000

How to Win

You win if you are the first to get four connected rectangles, like:

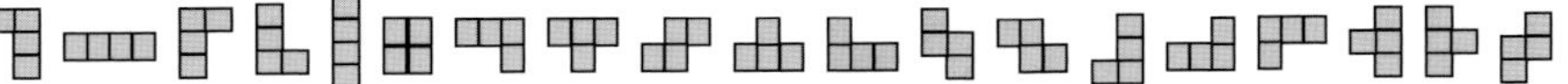

Play again!

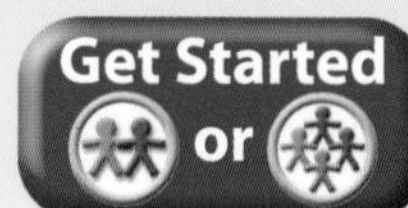

Get Started

Get 10 squares in one color and 10 in another color.
Get two number cubes. Take turns with another player or team.
Talk about math as you play!

At Your Turn

Toss two number cubes. Add the dots. Find your toss below.
Follow the directions. Explain your thinking. Cover the answer.
If the answer is taken, lose your turn. Have fun!

Toss	Read the word form of the number. Find the number in standard form.
2	Five thousand, two hundred fifty-two
3	Fifty-two thousand, five hundred twenty
4	Five hundred two thousand, five hundred twenty
5	Fifty-two million, fifty thousand, two
6	Fifty-two billion, five hundred twenty thousand
7	Fifty-two billion, five hundred million, twenty
8	Fifty-two billion, five hundred twenty million
9	Five million, two hundred fifty thousand, two
10	Five hundred twenty-five thousand, two hundred
11	Fifty-two thousand, fifty-two
12	Fifty-two thousand, five hundred two

52,050,002	5,252	52,520,000,000	52,000,520,000
52,502	5,250,002	52,052	525,200
52,000,520,000	52,500,000,020	52,520	5,250,002
52,520,000,000	502,520	52,050,002	52,500,000,020

How to Win

You win if you are the first to get four connected rectangles, like:

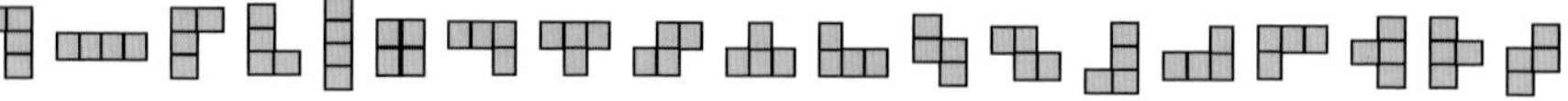

Play again!

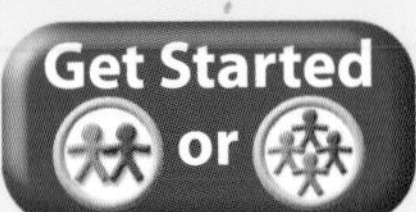

Get 10 squares in one color and 10 in another color.
Get two number cubes. Take turns with another player or team.
Talk about math as you play!

At Your Turn

Toss two number cubes. Add the dots. Find your toss below.
Follow the directions. Explain your thinking. Cover the answer.
If the answer is taken, lose your turn. Have fun!

Toss	Use paper and a pencil. Explain how to use division to write each fraction as a decimal.
2	$\frac{3}{5}$
3	$\frac{1}{5}$
4	$\frac{4}{5}$
5	$\frac{3}{4}$
6	$\frac{5}{10}$
7	$\frac{5}{100}$
8	$\frac{3}{10}$
9	$\frac{2}{5}$
10	$\frac{7}{100}$
11	$\frac{7}{10}$
12	$\frac{8}{10}$

0.6	0.4	0.75	0.8
0.7	0.5	0.2	0.07
0.3	0.8	0.3	0.5
0.05	0.75	0.4	0.05

You win if you are the first to get four connected rectangles, like:

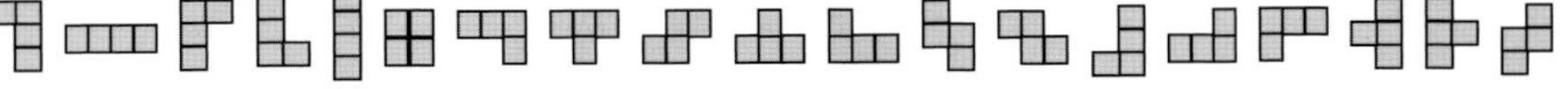

Play again!

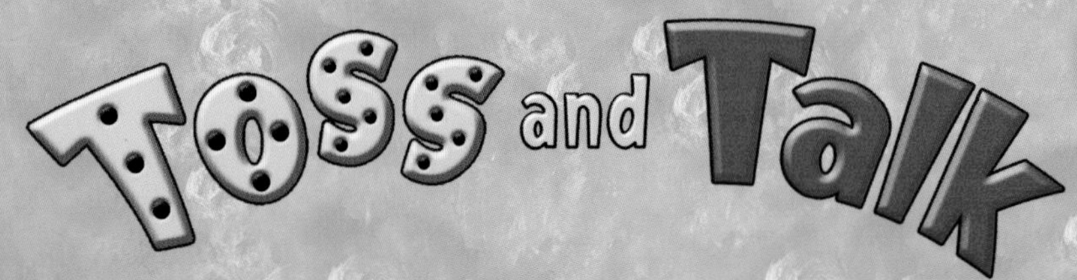

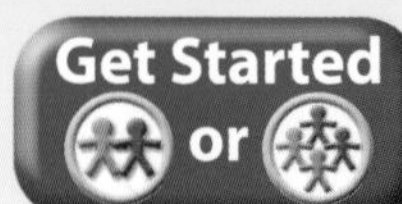

Get Started Get 10 squares in one color and 10 in another color. Get two number cubes. Take turns with another player or team. Talk about math as you play!

At Your Turn Toss two number cubes. Add the dots. Find your toss below. Follow the directions. Explain your thinking. Cover the answer. If the answer is taken, lose your turn. Have fun!

Toss	Explain how to show each fraction as a decimal. Use paper and a pencil if necessary.
2	$\frac{11}{50}$
3	$\frac{3}{25}$
4	$\frac{16}{50}$
5	$\frac{23}{100}$
6	$\frac{3}{20}$
7	$\frac{51}{100}$
8	$\frac{3}{4}$
9	$\frac{6}{25}$
10	$\frac{8}{25}$
11	$\frac{11}{100}$
12	$\frac{29}{50}$

0.22	0.15	0.51	0.23
0.75	0.32	0.23	0.32
0.24	0.58	0.75	0.12
0.51	0.11	0.24	0.15

How to Win You win if you are the first to get four connected rectangles, like:

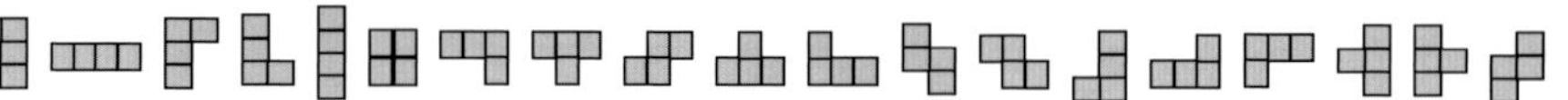

Play again!

Get 10 squares in one color and 10 in another color.
Get two number cubes. Take turns with another player or team.
Talk about math as you play!

At Your Turn

Toss two number cubes. Add the dots. Find your toss below.
Follow the directions. Explain your thinking. Cover the answer.
If the answer is taken, lose your turn. Have fun!

Toss	Read the question. Explain how to answer the question.
2	What is $\frac{250}{1,000}$ as a decimal?
3	What is $\frac{25}{1,000}$ as a decimal?
4	What is 0.025 as a fraction?
5	What is $\frac{15}{1,000}$ as a decimal?
6	What is $\frac{150}{1,000}$ as a decimal?
7	What is $\frac{5}{1,000}$ as a decimal?
8	What is 0.050 as a fraction?
9	What is $\frac{50}{1,000}$ as a decimal?
10	What is 0.250 as a fraction?
11	What is $\frac{2}{1,000}$ as a decimal?
12	What is 0.005 as a fraction?

$\frac{25}{1,000}$	$\frac{5}{1,000}$	0.15	$\frac{250}{1,000}$
0.15	0.050	0.25	0.002
0.025	0.005	0.005	$\frac{50}{1,000}$
0.050	0.015	$\frac{50}{1,000}$	0.015

You win if you are the first to get four connected rectangles, like:

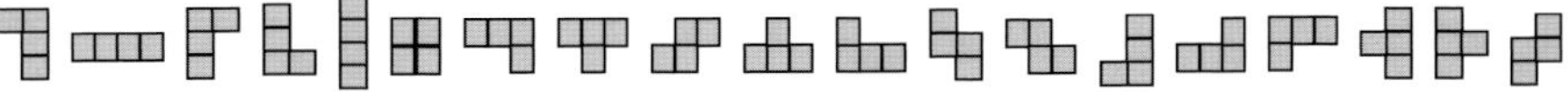

Play again!

Get Started 

Get 10 squares in one color and 10 in another color.
Get two number cubes. Take turns with another player or team.
Talk about math as you play!

At Your Turn

Toss two number cubes. Add the dots. Find your toss below.
Follow the directions. Explain your thinking. Cover the answer.
If the answer is taken, lose your turn. Have fun!

Toss	Read the question. Explain how to answer the question.
2	Is 0.560 the same as $\frac{56}{1{,}000}$?
3	What is 0.256 as a fraction?
4	What is $\frac{56}{1{,}000}$ as a decimal?
5	Is 0.560 the same as $\frac{560}{1{,}000}$?
6	If 256 acres of a farm are used to grow corn and the farm has 1,000 acres, what part of the farm grows corn? Express your answer as a decimal.
7	What is 0.250 as a fraction?
8	Is 0.056 the same as $\frac{56}{1{,}000}$?
9	What is the decimal for $\frac{25}{1{,}000}$?
10	What is $\frac{5}{1{,}000}$ as a decimal?
11	What is $\frac{506}{1{,}000}$ as a decimal?
12	Is $\frac{56}{100}$ the same as 0.056?

$\frac{256}{1{,}000}$	0.256	0.005	$\frac{250}{1{,}000}$
YES	YES	0.025	NO
0.056	0.025	0.256	$\frac{250}{1{,}000}$
NO	0.506	YES	YES

You win if you are the first to get four connected rectangles, like:

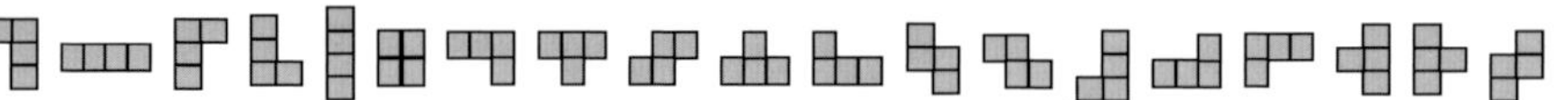

Play again!

Display the Digits

0 1 2 3 4 5 6 7 8 9

Read the question. Explain how to answer the question.
Display each 0 – 9 tile exactly once.
If you have a partner, take turns.

a. Which digit is in the thousandths place?

1.375126

b. Which digit is in the thousandths place?

7.514423

c. Which digit is in the tenths place?

5.957389

d. Which digit is in the tenths place?

8.12315

e. Which digit is in the thousandths place?

1.616567

f. Which digit is in the thousandths place?

2.4307

g. Which digit is in the hundredths place?

5.081279

h. Which digit is in the thousandths place?

3.3127234

i. Which digit is in the hundredths place?

5.432123

j. Which digit is in the hundredths place?

6.871275

Make up other questions about decimal place value.
Ask your partner to display the answers with 0 – 9 tiles.

Center Activity **1-4** ★★

Display the Digits

0 1 2 3 4 5 6 7 8 9

Read the question. Explain how to answer the question.
Display each 0 – 9 tile exactly once.
If you have a partner, take turns.

a. In the number five and two hundred fifty-three ten-thousandths, which digit is in the thousandths place?

b. In the number eighty-seven hundredths, which digit is in the tenths place?

c. In the number four and thirty-six thousandths, which digit is in the tenths place?

d. In the number three hundred eighty-four thousandths, which digit is in the thousandths place?

e. In the number six and eighteen thousandths, which digit is in the hundredths place?

f. In the number nine and two hundred sixty-seven thousandths, which digit is in the tenths place?

g. In the number sixty-seven thousandths, which digit is in the hundredths place?

h. In the number eight and two hundred ninety thousandths, which digit is in the hundredths place?

i. In the number five and thirty-seven millionths, which digit is in the hundred thousandths place?

j. In the number ninety-seven ten-thousandths, which digit is in the ten-thousandths place?

Make up other questions about decimal place value.
Ask your partner to display the answers with 0 – 9 tiles.

Teamwork

Put 1 2 3 4 in a bag.
Get paper and a pencil.

Repeat for Each Round

Choose **a**, **b**, **c**, **d**, **e**, or **f**.
Pick a tile. Pick two tiles if your group has only two students.
Do the jobs listed below in order.
To find your job, find the number that matches the tile you chose.

Write the numbers in a column, lining up the decimal points.

Say the least number. Explain why it is the least.

Say the greatest number. Explain why it is the greatest.

Order the numbers from least to greatest.

a.	5.532	5.352	5.523	b.	2.434	2.344	2.343
c.	3.125	3.512	3.152	d.	4.636	6.436	4.663
e.	9.324	9.234	9.342	f.	4.321	3.421	4.312

Work as a team. Write four decimals that each have three digits to the right of the decimal point. Repeat steps 1 – 4 for your decimals.

Teamwork

Get Started (or)

Get two number cubes, paper, and a pencil.
Put 1 2 3 4 in a bag.

Repeat for Each Round

Pick **a**, **b**, **c**, **d**, **e**, or **f**. Toss both cubes.
Pick a tile. Pick two tiles if your group has only two students.
Do the jobs listed below in order.
To find your job, find the number that matches the tile you chose.

 **Write the first number. Place the numbers you tossed in the blank spaces to make the greatest possible number.**

 **Write the second number. Place the numbers you tossed in the blank spaces to make the least possible number.**

 **Write the third number. Place the numbers you tossed in the blank spaces to make the greatest possible number.**

 **Order the three decimals from greatest to least.**

a. 5. □ 3 □ 5. 3 □ □ 5. □ □ 3	**b.** 2. 4 □ □ 2. □ 4 □ 2. □ □ 4	**c.** 3. □ □ 5 3. 5 □ □ 3. □ 5 □
d. 4. □ 3 □ □ 4 3 □ 4. □ □ 3	**e.** 9. □ 2 □ 9. 2 □ □ 9. □ □ 2	**f.** 4. □ □ 1 □ 1 □ 4 4. □ 1 □

If you have more time Repeat the activity. Have fun!

Display the Digits

0 1 2 3 4 5 6 7 8 9

Choose a row of numbers. Look at the numbers in the list.
Describe the pattern. Explain how to find the missing digits.
Use a number line to explain your answer. Say the numbers in order.
Display each 0 – 9 tile exactly once. If you have a partner, take turns.

0.29, 0.39, 0.49, 0.[a][b]

1.02, 1.03, 1.[c][d], 1.05

[e]0.2, 10.3, 10.4, 10.5, 10.[f]

0.00[g], 0.008, 0.009, 0.010

0.[h], 0.4, 0.6, 0.8

3.001, 3.002, 3.00[i], 3.004

60.6, 70.7, 80.[j], 90.9

a	b	c	d	e
f	g	h	i	j

Make up other lists that show patterns with decimal numbers.
Ask your partner to display the missing digits with 0 – 9 tiles.

Choose a row of numbers. Look at the numbers in the list. Describe the pattern. Explain how to find the missing digits. Use a number line to explain your answer. Say the numbers in order. Display each 0 – 9 tile exactly once. If you have a partner, take turns.

12.2, 24.4, 48.[a], 97.6

10.9, 11.9, 13.9, 16.9, 2[b].[c]

0.010, 0.009, 0.008, 0.00[d], 0.006

90, 90.2, 90.[e], 90.6, 90.8

28.8, 28.[f], 28.4, 28.[g], 28.0

0.9, [h].8, 2.7, [i].6, 4.5, 5.4

1, 0.50, 0.2[j], 0.125

a	b	c	d	e
f	g	h	i	j

Make up other lists that show patterns with decimal numbers. Ask your partner to display the missing digits with 0 – 9 tiles.

Quick Questions

Get Started

Each player tosses two number cubes.
If your numbers match another player's numbers, toss again.
Decide who will read the first question. Take turns.

For Each Question

Listen to the reader. Compute mentally. Discuss how to use compensation or a Property when you compute. Agree on the correct answer. Every player who has that answer can remove one cube that shows the answer.

How to Win

The first player who removes both cubes wins. Have fun!

Use mental math.

a	Add 19 + 24. Which digit is in the tens place?
b	Subtract 87 - 19. Which digit is in the tens place?
c	Add 25 + 56 + 4. Which digit is in the ones place?
d	Subtract 76 - 39. Which digit is in the tens place?
e	Add 87 + 3 + 43. Which digit is in the ones place?
f	Subtract 68 - 19. Which digit is in the tens place?
g	Add 279 + 412. Which digit is in the ones place?
h	Subtract 131 - 89. Which digit is in the tens place?
i	Add 32 + 36 + 4. Which digit is in the ones place?
j	Subtract 252 - 38. Which digit is in the tens place?
k	Add 86 + 33 + 4. Which digit is in the tens place?
l	Subtract 734 - 59. Which digit is in the ones place?
m	Add 27 + 32 + 3. Which digit is in the tens place?

n	Subtract 36 - 19. Which digit is in the tens place?
o	Add 41 + 9 + 12. Which digit is in the tens place?
p	Subtract 368 - 142. Which digit is in the tens place?
q	Add 25 + 86 + 4. Which digit is in the tens place?
r	Subtract 41 - 18. Which digit is in the ones place?
s	Add 67 + 3 + 54. Which digit is in the tens place?
t	Subtract 252 - 88. Which digit is in the tens place?
u	Add 39 + 16. Which digit is in the tens place?
v	Subtract 48 - 29. Which digit is in the tens place?
w	Add 399 + 44 + 1. Which digit is in the tens place?
x	Subtract 252 - 98. Which digit is in the tens place?
y	Add 137 + 95 + 5. Which digit is in the tens place?
z	Add 96 + 39. Which digit is in the ones place?

Toss two number cubes again. Play another game.
Begin with the next question in the list.

Quick Questions

Get Started

Each player tosses two number cubes.
If your numbers match another player's numbers, toss again.
Decide who will read the first question. Take turns.

For Each Question

Listen to the reader. Compute mentally. Discuss how to use compensation or a Property when you compute. Agree on the correct answer. Every player who has that answer can remove one cube that shows the answer.

How to Win

The first player who removes both cubes wins. Have fun!

Use mental math.

a	Add 117 + 52 + 3. Which digit is in the hundreds place?	n	Subtract 846 - 124. Which digit is in the tens place?
b	Subtract 533 - 77. Which digit is in the tens place?	o	Add 477 + 3 + 217. Which digit is in the hundreds place?
c	Add 431 + 22 + 9. Which digit is in the hundreds place?	p	Subtract 346 -93. Which digit is in the tens place?
d	Subtract 621 - 59. Which digit is in the tens place?	q	Add 368 + 77 + 2. Which digit is in the hundreds place?
e	Add 337 + 245 + 5. Which digit is in the hundreds place?	r	Subtract 445 - 35. Which digit is in the tens place?
f	Subtract 458 - 32. Which digit is in the tens place?	s	Add 136 + 248 + 4. Which digit is in the hundreds place?
g	Add 299 + 34 + 1. Which digit is in the hundreds place?	t	Subtract 881 - 453. Which digit is in the tens place?
h	Subtract 977 - 263. Which digit is in the tens place?	u	Add 479 + 13 + 1. Which digit is in the hundreds place?
i	Add 537 + 95 + 5. Which digit is in the hundreds place?	v	Subtract 848 - 632. Which digit is in the tens place?
j	Subtract 846 - 24. Which digit is in the tens place?	w	Add 345 + 232 + 5. Which digit is in the hundreds place?
k	Add 464 + 19 + 1. Which digit is in the hundreds place?	x	Subtract 599 - 61. Which digit is in the tens place?
l	Subtract 444 - 76. Which digit is in the tens place?	y	Add 374 + 34 + 36. Which digit is in the hundreds place?
m	Add 148 + 217 + 3. Which digit is in the hundreds place?	z	Subtract 999 - 89. Which digit is in the tens place?

Play another game. Begin with the next question in the list.
Or make up your own questions like these. Play the game with your questions.

Display the Digits

0 1 2 3 4 5 6 7 8 9

Explain the steps for rounding. Say the rounded number. Answer the question. Display each 0 – 9 tile exactly once. If you have a partner, take turns.

a. If you round <u>6</u>87 to the place of the underlined digit, which digit will be in that place? ☐

b. If you round 3<u>5</u>.8 to the place of the underlined digit, which digit will be in that place? ☐

c. If you round 9,<u>0</u>65 to the place of the underlined digit, which digit will be in that place? ☐

d. If you round 8<u>7</u>.73 to the place of the underlined digit, which digit will be in that place? ☐

e. If you round 3,5<u>2</u>7 to the place of the underlined digit, which digit will be in that place? ☐

f. If you round 68<u>3</u>.92 to the place of the underlined digit, which digit will be in that place? ☐

g. If you round 82<u>1</u>,998 to the place of the underlined digit, which digit will be in that place? ☐

h. If you round 2<u>0</u>.2 to the place of the underlined digit, which digit will be in that place? ☐

i. If you round <u>4</u>9,206 to the place of the underlined digit, which digit will be in that place? ☐

j. If you round <u>8</u>.67 to the place of the underlined digit, which digit will be in that place? ☐

Make up other questions like these.
Ask your partner to display the answers with 0 – 9 tiles.

Display the Digits

0 1 2 3 4 5 6 7 8 9

Explain the steps for rounding. Say the rounded number. Answer the question. Display each 0 – 9 tile exactly once. If you have a partner, take turns.

a. When you round 25.876 to the nearest one, which digit is in the ones place?

b. When you round 642,200.64 to the nearest one, which digit is in the ones place?

c. When you round 845,746.9 to the nearest hundred, which digit is in the hundreds place?

d. When you round 64.196 to the nearest tenth, which digit is in the tenths place?

e. When you round 525,326.22 to the nearest hundred thousand, which digit is in the hundred thousands place?

f. When you round 420.578 to the nearest hundredth, which digit is in the hundredths place?

g. When you round 34,208.899 to the nearest thousand, which digit is in the thousands place?

h. When you round 4,590.016 to the nearest tenth, which digit is in the tenths place?

i. When you round 98.87 to the nearest tenth, which digit is in the tenths place?

j. When you round 5,670.525 to the nearest hundredth, which digit is in the hundredths place?

Make up other questions like these. Ask your partner to display the answers with 0 – 9 tiles.

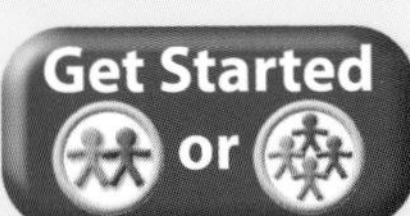

Put 1 2 3 4 in a bag.

For Each Round

Choose A, B, C, D, E, or F.
Pick a tile. Pick two tiles if your group has only two students.
Evaluate the expression next to your number. Explain your thinking.
Discuss: Which three expressions have the same estimate? Why?
Decide: Which expression has a different estimate? Why?

A	Estimate the sum. Round each addend to the nearest ten.
1	38 + 64
2	52 + 49
3	74 + 28
4	64 + 29

B	Estimate the difference. Round each number to the nearest ten.
1	64 – 31
2	72 – 44
3	42 – 12
4	53 – 27

C	Estimate the sum. Round each decimal to the nearest whole number.
1	7.1 + 4.7 + 3.9
2	4.8 + 5.7 + 3.6
3	2.8 + 9.1 + 3.7
4	4.7 + 3.6 + 6.6

D	Estimate the difference. Round each decimal to the nearest whole number.
1	52.11 – 9.98
2	64.13 – 17.76
3	96.44 – 53.72
4	78.62 – 37.12

E	Estimate the sum. Round each decimal to the nearest whole number.
1	68.9 + 82.34
2	67.81 + 72.44
3	72.14 + 78.95
4	88.6 + 62.34

F	Estimate the difference. Round each number to the nearest thousand.
1	4,856 – 2,257
2	8,100 – 4,795
3	6,177 – 1,984
4	6,845 – 3,888

Make up a "Think Together" question for this lesson.
Challenge your classmates to think together to answer your question.

Put 1 2 3 4 in a bag.

For Each Round

Choose A, B, or C.
Pick a tile. Pick two tiles if your group has only two students.
Follow the directions next to your number.
Discuss: How did your group estimate to answer your question?
Decide: Is each estimate reasonable?

A Al's Market	
Vegetables	$3.89
Chicken	$14.50
Paper Plates	$5.59
Fruit	$8.76

B Bob's Grocery	
Vegetables	$2.15
Chicken	$9.89
Paper Plates	$10.45
Fruit	$11.24

C Cost Saver Convenience Store	
Vegetables	$4.45
Chicken	$8.45
Paper Plates	$8.19
Fruit	$5.20

Do These Steps in Order

 **Ask a question about the data so that your group can estimate the cost for two picnic items.**

 **Ask a different question so that your group can estimate the cost for two picnic items other than those chosen in step 1.**

 **Ask a question about the data so that your group can estimate the difference between the cost of two different items.**

 **Ask a question about the data so that your group can estimate the cost for three picnic items.**

Make up a "Think Together" question for this lesson.
Challenge your classmates to think together to answer your question.

Teamwork

Read about the Muffin Factory.

Repeat for Each Round

Choose a week. Work together.
Tap on each type of container to show how many each group needs.
Explain how the two groups can combine their purchases to get the fewest number of containers each week. Say your answer as a decimal.

THE MUFFIN FACTORY

Buy our boxes, packs, or single muffins.

Buy and Save Today!

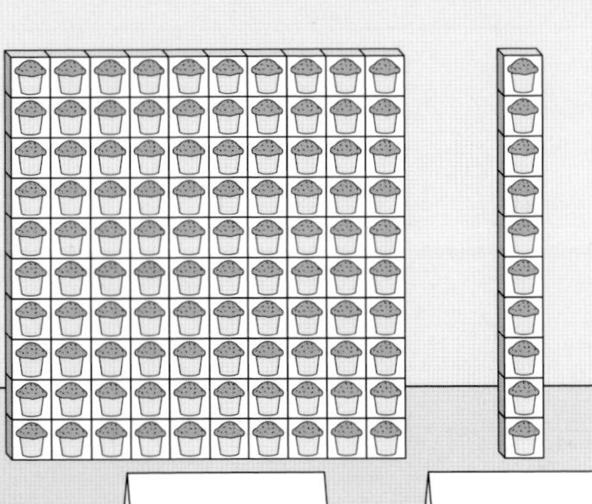

1 Whole box   0.1 of a box   0.01 of a box

Containers Needed

	Group	
	Glee Club	Band
Week 1	1.43	1.07
Week 2	2.92	1.46
Week 3	2.15	0.85
Week 4	1.75	1.65

How much more does the Glee Club need than the band each week? Explain how to regroup the containers as needed so you can compare. Give your answer as a decimal.

Teamwork

Read about the Muffin Factory.
Put 0 1 2 3 4 5 6 7 8 9 in a bag.
Work together.

Repeat for Each Round

Pick 4 tiles.
Arrange the tiles in the squares below to get the greatest possible sum.
Arrange the same tiles to get the greatest possible difference.

THE MUFFIN FACTORY

Buy our boxes, packs, or single muffins.

Buy and Save Today!

Buy a box! Buy a pack! Buy a single muffin!

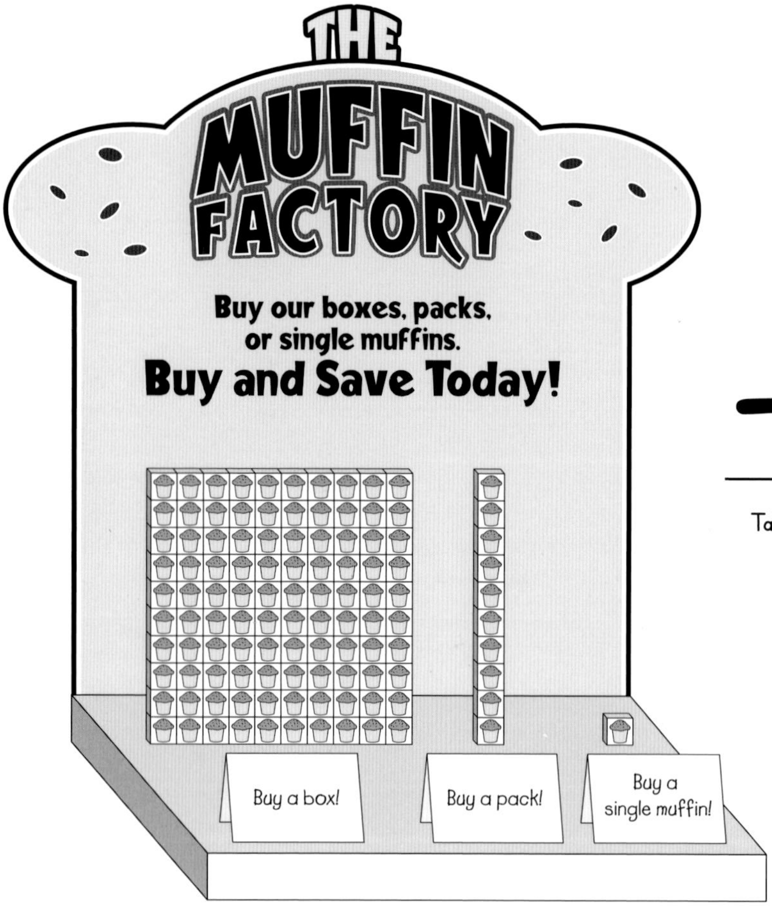

1 Whole box 0.1 of a box 0.01 of a box

Buy Two Amounts

	1. ☐ ☐
+	1. ☐ ☐

Talk about making two purchases at the muffin factory. Explain why you have the greatest possible sum.

Compare Two Amounts

	1. ☐ ☐
−	0. ☐ ☐

Talk about comparing two purchases at the muffin factory. Explain why you have the greatest possible difference.

Put the tiles in the bag. Try again.

Teamwork

Get Started or

Put 1 2 3 4 5 6 in a bag.
Get paper and a pencil. Take turns.

Repeat for Each Round

Pick a tile. Read the problem next to your tile number. Find the picture below that fits your problem. Explain why you chose that picture. Ask your team to write and solve an equation for your problem. Decide on the correct answer and explain why it is reasonable.

Alice buys 8 apples. She needs 22 apples in all. How many more apples should Alice get?

Bob and Bill have a total of 22 dollars. Bob has 14 dollars. How many dollars does Bill have?

John and Nancy were in a rowboat. John rowed 18 miles and Nancy rowed 4 miles. How far did John and Nancy row?

Carol brought 4 more CDs to the party than Tom did. Tom brought 9 CDs. How many CDs did they bring in all?

A shirt costs $22. Jim paid $16 for the shirt when it was on sale. How much did Jim save?

Jane saved 22 dollars for gifts. She has 5 dollars left after buying 3 gifts. How much did all 3 gifts cost?

Total	Parts
x	9 | 13
22	14 | x
x	18 | 4
22	x | 5
22	16 | x
22	8 | x

If you have more time

Make up a problem that your team can solve by drawing a picture and writing an equation.

Teamwork

Get 1 2 3 4 5 6 7 8.
Get paper and a pencil. Take turns

Repeat for Each Round

Choose **A, B, C,** or **D**. Read the question. Find the picture that helps you to solve the problem. Display number tiles below to show the missing number in the equation. Ask your team to solve the equation. Decide if the answer is reasonable.

A. Jim has 50 apples. He gives 20 to Susan and 14 to Adam. How many apples does Jim have left?

B. Bill gives away 65 pencils and has 19 left. How many did Bill start with?

C. A clown split 72 balloons into 2 bunches. One bunch had 36 balloons. How many balloons were in the other bunch?

D. A clown started with 72 balloons to give away. The clown had 18 left after an hour. How many balloons did the clown give away in that hour?

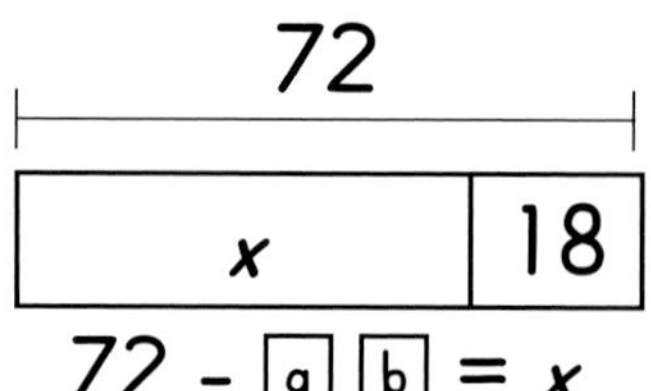

72 - [a] [b] = x

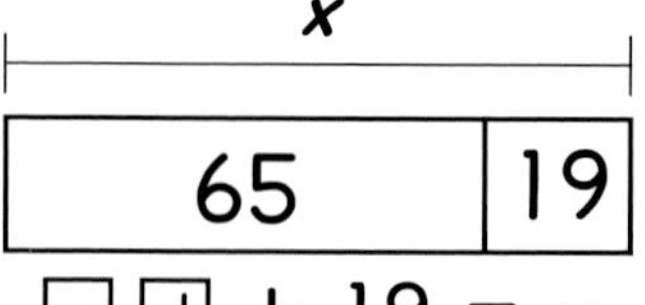

[c] [d] + 19 = x

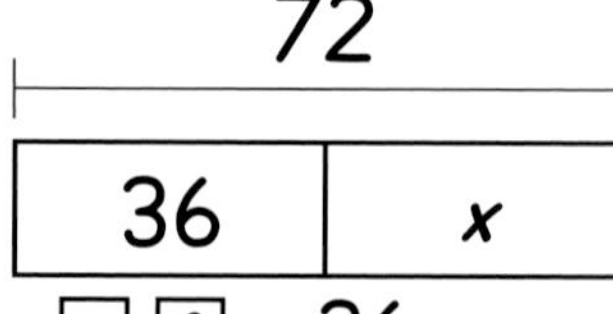

[e] [f] - 36 = x

50

x	14	20

x + [g] [h] = 50

a	b	c	d
e	f	g	h

Make up a problem that your team can solve by drawing a picture and writing an equation.

Get Started Get 10 squares in one color and 10 in another color, two paper clips, and two number cubes. Take turns.

At Your Turn Toss two cubes to find your ovals. **EXAMPLE:** Choose the 3rd oval on the left and the 5th oval on the right, **or** choose the 5th oval on the left and the 3rd oval on the right. Mark your ovals with paper clips.

How to Play Explain how to add the two numbers you chose. Find and cover the answer. Lose your turn if the answer is taken.

How to Win The first player or team to get any three connected rectangles in a row or column wins.

Left ovals					Right ovals
15.3	9.8	5.695	21.06	2.65	0.05
4.87	28.205	24.1	39.465	21.055	18.46
21.005	12.07	7.965	23.33	4.92	3.095
2.6	22.5	18.395	33.76	15.35	7.2
4.87					3.095
21.005					18.46

If you have more time Play again! Talk about how you know that your answer is reasonable.

Clip and Cover

Get 10 squares in one color and 10 in another color, one paper clip, and one number cube. Take turns.

At Your Turn Toss one cube to find your oval. **EXAMPLE:** Choose the 3rd oval on the left, **or** choose the 3rd oval on the right. Mark your oval with a paper clip.

How to Play The number you chose is a sum. Find two numbers that you can add to get that sum. Cover the answer. Lose your turn if the answer is taken.

How to Win The first player or team to get any three connected rectangles in a row or column wins.

Left ovals					Right ovals
37.08	33.5 + 41.71	28.308 + 31.702	58.39 + 8.34	12.093 + 15.006	88.701
17.49	73.2 + 5.264	13.68 + 23.4	27.4 + 32.61	56.45 + 32.876	66.73
47.81	13.972 + 13.127	4.001 + 84.7	56.8 + 26.73	64.116 + 25.21	89.326
83.53	35.24 + 12.57	23.87 + 13.21	17.3 + 14.608	7.085 + 10.405	78.464
27.099					31.908
75.21					60.01

Play again! Talk about your strategies as you play.

Teamwork

Get Started  Put 1 2 3 4 in a bag.

Repeat for Each Round Choose **a, b, c, d, e,** or **f**. Pick a tile. Pick two tiles if your group has only two students. Do the jobs listed below in order. To find your job, find the number that matches the tile you chose. Put the tiles back in the bag before beginning the next round.

1. **Estimate the difference.**
2. **Explain how to subtract the hundredths.**
3. **Explain how to subtract the tenths.**
4. **Explain how to subtract the whole numbers.**

☆☆☆ Subtract ☆☆☆

a.	\$19.12 - \$1.28	b.	\$68.94 - \$2.89
c.	\$24.10 - \$4.50	d.	\$37.40 - \$3.13
e.	\$17.50 - \$3.65	f.	\$55.45 - \$5.75

If you have more time Choose any other two amounts of money. Pick tiles again. Follow steps 1 – 4 for your amounts of money.

Teamwork

Put 0 1 2 3 4 5 6 7 8 9 in a bag.

Repeat for Each Round

Pick five tiles. Fill the squares for the first number. Let your partner, or the other team, pick tiles to fill the squares for the other number. Make sure that the first number is greater than the second number. Take turns doing the steps below in order. Put the tiles back in the bag before beginning the next round.

STEP 1 **Estimate the difference.**

STEP 2 **Explain how to subtract the thousandths.**

STEP 3 **Explain how to subtract the hundredths.**

STEP 4 **Explain how to subtract the tenths.**

STEP 5 **Explain how to subtract the ones.**

STEP 6 **Explain how to subtract the tens.**

STEP 7 **Say the difference.**

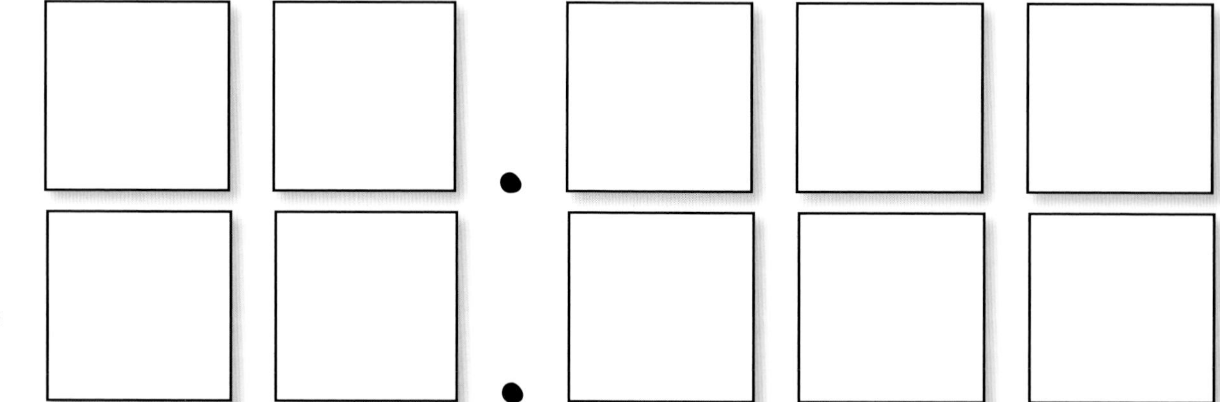

Give examples to explain why someone might need to subtract two numbers like these.

Choose a problem. Read it. Explain how to answer the hidden questions. Solve the problem. Use tiles to show each answer below. Display each 0 – 9 tile exactly once. If you have a partner, take turns.

Bonnie buys six apples that cost $0.59 each, and three bananas that cost $0.26 each. How much money does she spend in all? How many items does she buy?

$ [a] . [b]4 for six $ [c] . [d]8 for three

Total Cost = $4.3 [e]   Number of Items [f]

During the summer, Sal works 6 hours each day, Monday through Friday. On Saturdays and Sundays, he works 2 more hours each day. How many more hours does he work during the week (Monday through Friday) than on the weekends (Saturday and Sunday)?

[g] x 5 days M-F   [h] x 2 days S-S

[i] [j] more hours during the week

a	b	c	d	e
f	g	h	i	j

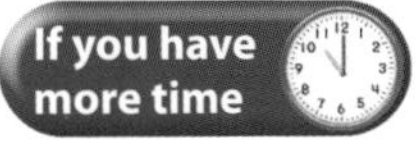

Make up other problems that have more than one step. Ask your partner to display the answers with 0 – 9 tiles.

Choose a problem. Read it. Explain how to answer the hidden questions. Solve the problem. Use tiles to show each answer. Display each 0 – 9 tile exactly once. If you have a partner, take turns.

Hakeem makes $6 an hour and worked 26 hours last week. His sister, Hadja, earns $8 an hour and worked 17 hours last week. How much more money did Hakeem earn? Write an equation to show your steps.

$1 [a] 6 – $ [b] [c] [d]

= $ [e] [f]

Melanie purchases two identical sweaters. She has a $10 coupon. What is the cost of one sweater if her total bill after the coupon is subtracted is $85.96?

$ [g] [h] . [i] [j]

Make up other problems that have more than one step. Ask your partner to display the answers with 0 – 9 tiles.

Get 10 squares in one color and 10 in another color.
Get two number cubes. Take turns with another player or team.
Talk about math as you play!

At Your Turn

Toss two number cubes. Add the dots. Find your toss below.
Follow the directions. Explain your thinking. Cover the answer.
If the answer is taken, lose your turn. Have fun!

Toss	Read the equation. Name the Property of Multiplication used in the equation. Explain.
2	(5 × 8) × 6 = 5 × (8 × 6)
3	0 × 27 = 0
4	17 × 113 = 113 × 17
5	1 × 83 = 83
6	3 × (12 × 20) = 3 × (20 × 12) = (3 × 20) × 12
7	(1 × 6) × 9 = 1 × (6 × 9) = 6 × 9
8	3 × 12 = 12 × 3
9	(1 × 6) x 5 = 6 × 5
10	(3 × 7) × 2 = 2 × (3 × 7)
11	(0 × 5) × 7 = 0 × (5 × 7) = 0
12	1 × 0 = 0

Commutative Property	Identity Property and Zero Property	Zero Property	Identity Property
Associative Property and Zero Property	Commutative Property and Associative Property	Associative Property and Identity Property	Commutative Property
Identity Property	Commutative Property	Associative Property	Identity Property
Associative Property and Identity Property	Identity Property	Commutative Property	Commutative Property and Associative Property

You win if you are the first to get four connected rectangles, like:

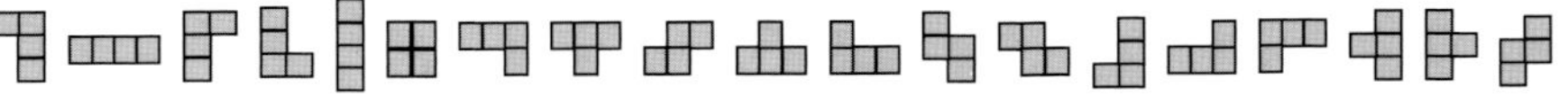

Play again!

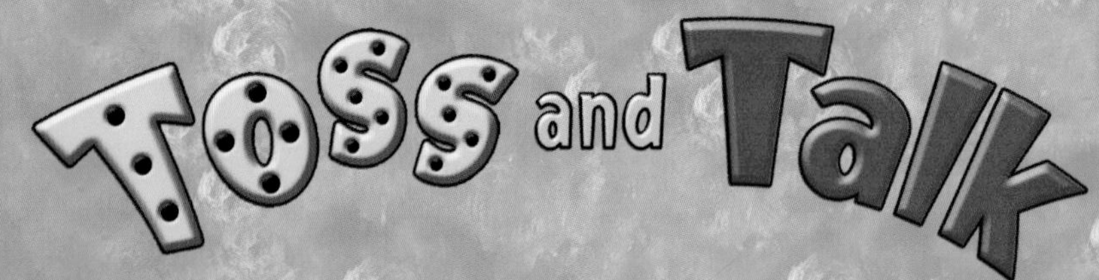

Get 10 squares in one color and 10 in another color.
Get two number cubes. Take turns with another player or team.
Talk about math as you play!

At Your Turn

Toss two number cubes. Add the dots. Find your toss below.
Follow the directions. Explain your thinking. Cover the answer.
If the answer is taken, lose your turn. Have fun!

Toss	Read what is given. Find an equation that uses that Property or those Properties of Multiplication. Explain your choice.
2	Commutative Property and Zero Property
3	Associative Property and Identity Property
4	Associative Property
5	Commutative Property
6	Zero Property and Commutative Property
7	Associative Property and Zero Property
8	Identity Property
9	Commutative Property and Associative Property
10	Zero Property
11	Commutative Property and Identity Property
12	Identity Property and Zero Property

$(3 \times 13) \times 0 = 3 \times (13 \times 0) = 3 \times 0$	$3 \times (92 \times 1) = 3 \times 92$	$9 \times (13 \times 0) = 9 \times 0 = 0 \times 9$	$27 \times 131 = 131 \times 27$
$19 \times (3 \times 17) = (19 \times 3) \times 17$	$(18 \times 62) \times 31 = (62 \times 18) \times 31 = 62 \times (18 \times 31)$	$(0 \times 18) \times 96 = 0 \times 96 = 96 \times 0$	$1 \times 0 = 0$
$13 \times 76 = 76 \times 13$	$0 \times (56 \times 27) = 0$	$(17 \times 12) \times 1 = 1 \times (17 \times 12) = (17 \times 12)$	$(0 \times 7) \times 18 = 0 \times 18 = 18 \times 0$
$(1 \times 52) \times 20 = 1 \times (52 \times 20) = 52 \times 20$	$(3 \times 9) \times 14 = 14 \times (3 \times 9) = (14 \times 3) \times 9$	$(0 \times 9) \times 11 = 0 \times (9 \times 11) = 0$	$1 \times (7 \times 16) = 7 \times 16$

How to Win

You win if you are the first to get four connected rectangles, like:

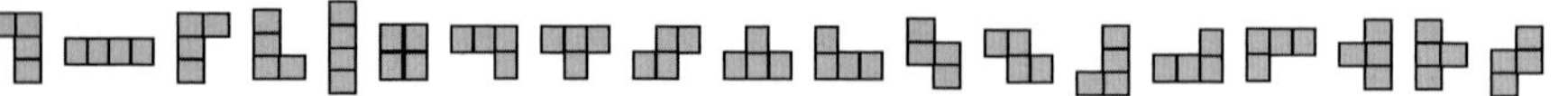

Play again!

Get 10 squares in one color and 10 in another color.
Get two number cubes. Take turns with another player or team.
Talk about math as you play!

At Your Turn

Toss two number cubes. Add the dots. Find your toss below.
Follow the directions. Explain your thinking. Cover the answer.
If the answer is taken, lose your turn. Have fun!

Toss	Explain how to use mental math, properties, and patterns to multiply the factors. Find the product.
2	600 × 2,000
3	60 × 20 × 10
4	600 × 20 × 0
5	500 × 20 × 100
6	4 × 5 × 500
7	4 × 25 × 1,000
8	5 × 40 × 10,000
9	2 × 55 × 1,000
10	3 × 200 × 200
11	20 × 60
12	4 × 1 × 250

1,200,000	1,000,000	12,000	120,000
10,000	1,200	0	100,000
100,000	2,000,000	1,000	2,000,000
110,000	1,000,000	110,000	10,000

You win if you are the first to get four connected rectangles, like:

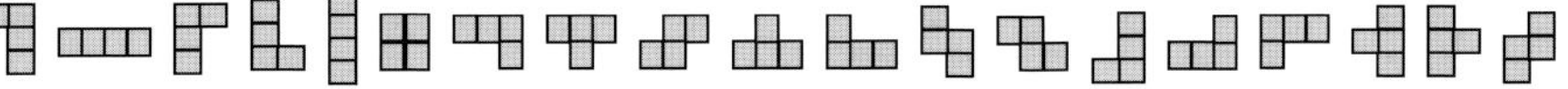

Play again!

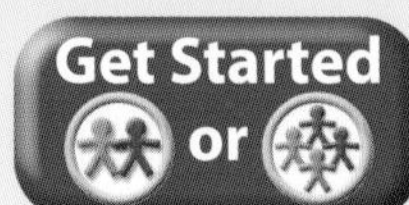

Get 10 squares in one color and 10 in another color.
Get two number cubes. Take turns with another player or team.
Talk about math as you play!

At Your Turn

Toss two number cubes. Add the dots. Find your toss below.
Follow the directions. Explain your thinking. Cover the answer.
If the answer is taken, lose your turn. Have fun!

Toss	Read the number. Find a way to multiply so that the product is that number. Explain your choice of factors.
2	6,000
3	60,000
4	6,000,000
5	10,600
6	36,000
7	3,600,000
8	360,000
9	106,000
10	1,600,000
11	160,000
12	16,000

40 × 9,000	30 × 2,000	40 × 90 × 10	30 × 30 × 4,000
400 × 30 × 300	2 × 53 × 100	400 × 200 × 20	400 × 900
400 × 90	40 × 200 × 20	4 × 100 × 40	200 × 30
20 × 53 × 100	10 × 53 × 200	53 × 50 × 4	300 × 200 × 100

You win if you are the first to get four connected rectangles, like:

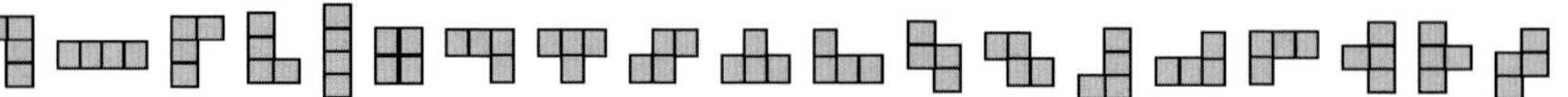

Play again!

Get Started (or): Get 10 squares in one color and 10 in another color, two paper clips, and two number cubes. Take turns.

At Your Turn: Toss two cubes to find your ovals. **EXAMPLE:** Choose the 3rd oval on the left and the 5th oval on the right, **or** choose the 5th oval on the left and the 3rd oval on the right. Mark your ovals with paper clips.

How to Play: Round each factor to the nearest ten. Estimate the product. Find and cover the estimate. Lose your turn if the answer is taken.

How to Win: The first player or team to get any three connected rectangles in a row or column wins.

Left ovals: 91, 25, 82, 56, 89, 34

1,800	600	1,600	1,200
900	300	800	600
4,500	1,500	4,000	3,000
3,600	1,200	3,200	2,400

Right ovals: 16, 13, 48, 37, 5, 54

If you have more time: Play again! Explain how you round each factor.

Get Started or

Get 10 squares in one color and 10 in another color, one paper clip, and one number cube. Take turns.

At Your Turn Toss one cube to find your oval. **EXAMPLE:** Choose the 3rd oval on the left, **or** choose the 3rd oval on the right. Mark your oval with a paper clip.

How to Play If you multiply the rounded numbers you chose to estimate a product, what could the original factors be? Explain your choice. Cover the factors. Lose your turn if the answer is taken.

How to Win The first player or team to get any three connected rectangles in a row or column wins.

Left ovals					Right ovals
60 × 70 20 × 300	147 × 12	69 × 81	52 × 27	125 × 38	50 × 30 70 × 80
500 × 90	245 × 113	84 × 76	61 × 69	305 × 45	80 × 80
150 × 10	46 × 33	23 × 32	313 × 54	67 × 76	20 × 30
300 × 50 100 × 40	22 × 29	47 × 53	18 × 304	504 × 87	50 × 50 250 × 100

Play again! Talk about how your strategies as you play.

Tic Tac Toe

Get Started Get paper and a pencil. Get 20 squares in one color and 20 in another color. Get two number cubes for players to share. Take turns.

For Each Round Toss one cube. Use that number as your base. Toss the other cube. Use that number as an exponent for your base. ***Say the number in expanded form. Find the standard form for that number.*** Cover the number in standard form. If the answer is taken, lose your turn.

Example **3** is the base. **5** is the exponent.
3^5 Say: 3 x 3 x 3 x 3 x 3. The standard form for that number is 243.

How to Win The first player or team to cover a row, column, or diagonal in one of the four sections of the game board wins.

16	243	25	1	4	3
15,625	2	16	81	5	4
729	3,125	1	216	64	6
9	1	1,024	1,296	256	1
4,096	64	32	125	625	7,776
1	36	46,656	27	1	8

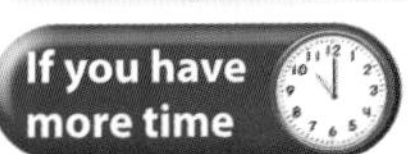

Play again!

Tic Tac Toe

Get Started 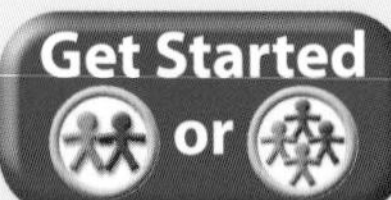 Get paper and a pencil. Get 20 squares in one color and 20 in another color. Get one number cube for players to share. Take turns.

For Each Round Toss one cube. Use that number as your base.
Choose 1, 2, 3, 4, 5, or 6 as an exponent for your base.
Say your number in expanded form and in standard form.
Cover the number in standard form. If the answer is taken, lose your turn.

Example The base is **3**. Choose $\mathbf{3}^1$, $\mathbf{3}^2$, $\mathbf{3}^3$, $\mathbf{3}^4$, $\mathbf{3}^5$, or $\mathbf{3}^6$ depending on which space you want to cover on the game board.
If you choose $\mathbf{3}^4$, then say 3 x 3 x 3 x 3 is 81.

How to Win The first player or team to cover a row, column, or diagonal in one of the four sections of the game board wins.

1,296	243	6	36	1	1,024
32	64	1	4	7,776	3
25	1	46,656	4	1	729
64	3,125	27	125	2	256
16	9	625	1	216	5
1	15,625	8	4,096	81	16

Play again!

Teamwork

Get paper and a pencil.
Put 1 2 3 4 5 6 in a bag.

Repeat for Each Round

Pick four tiles. Arrange them in the squares below to form 2-digit factors.
Take turns as you do the steps listed below in order.
Put the tiles back in the bag for the next round.

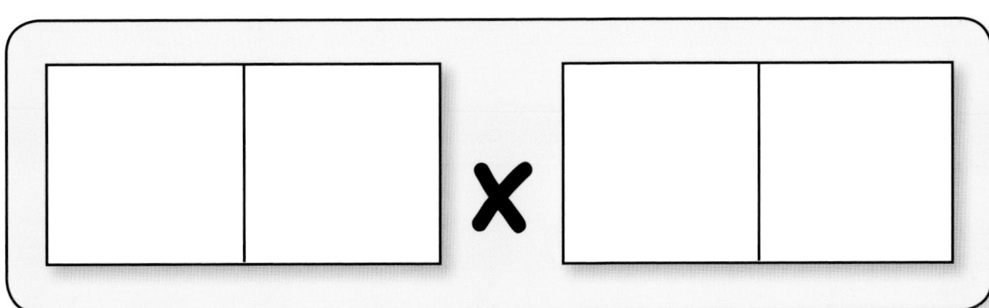

STEP 1 **Write the first factor as the sum of two numbers.**

STEP 2 **Apply the distributive property using the numbers given in step 1. Work with your team. Find the product.**

STEP 3 **Write the second factor as the sum of two numbers.**

STEP 4 **Apply the distributive property using the numbers given in step 3. Work with your team. Find the product. Make sure the product is the same as in step 2.**

Make up a multiplication problem.
Ask your team to use the distributive property to find the product.

Teamwork

Get paper and a pencil.
Put 1 2 3 4 5 6 7 8 9 in a bag.

Pick four tiles. Arrange them in the squares below to form 2-digit factors.
Take turns as you do the steps listed below in order.
Put the tiles back in the bag for the next round.

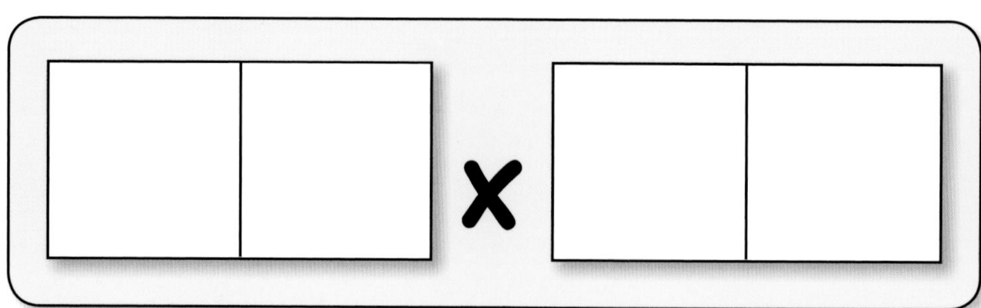

STEP 1 **Write the first factor as the sum or difference of two numbers.**

STEP 2 **Apply the distributive property using the numbers given in step 1. Work with your team. Find the product.**

STEP 3 **Write the second factor as the sum or difference of two numbers.**

STEP 4 **Apply the distributive property using the numbers given in step 3. Work with your team. Find the product. Make sure the product is the same as in step 2.**

Make up a multiplication problem.
Ask your team to use the distributive property to find the product.

Display the Digits

0 1 2 3 4 5 6 7 8 9

Explain how to multiply the ones and how to multiply the tens.
Display each 0 – 9 tile exactly once. If you have a partner, take turns.
For each problem below, there are 36 toy cars in each box.

a. If there are 6 boxes of cars, how many cars are there in all? Which digit is in the hundreds place in the answer?

b. If there are 4 boxes of cars, how many cars are there in all? Which digit is in the tens place in the answer?

c. If there are 7 boxes of cars, how many cars are there in all? Which digit is in the tens place in the answer?

d. If I have 108 cars in all, how many boxes of 36 cars do I have?

e. If there are 2 boxes of cars, how many cars are there in all? Which digit is in the tens place in the answer?

f. If there are 8 boxes of cars, how many cars are there in all? Which digit is in the ones place in the answer?

g. If there are 4 boxes of cars, how many cars are there in all? Which digit is in the hundreds place in the answer?

h. If I have 324 cars in all, how many boxes of 36 cars do I have?

i. If there are 5 boxes of cars, how many cars are there in all? Which digit is in the ones places in the answer?

j. If there are 6 boxes of cars, how many cars are there in all? Which digit is in the ones place in the answer?

Make up other questions about multiplication.
Ask your partner to display the answers with 0 – 9 tiles.

Display the Digits

0 1 2 3 4 5 6 7 8 9

Use estimation to help you find the missing factor. Multiply to check. Display each 0 – 9 tile exactly once. If you have a partner, take turns.

a. If the product is 228 and one factor is 57, what is the other factor? ☐

b. If the product is 0 and one factor is 398, what is the other factor? ☐

c. If the product is 288 and one factor is 48, what is the other factor? ☐

d. If $9 \times (7 \times \square) = 504$, what is the missing factor? ☐

e. If the product is 72 and one factor is 36, what is the other factor? ☐

f. If the product is 495 and one factor is 99, what is the other factor? ☐

g. If the product is 329 and one factor is 47, what is the other factor? ☐

h. If $(6 \times 7) \times \square) = 378$, what is the missing factor? ☐

i. If the product is 246 and one factor is 246, what is the other factor? ☐

j. If the product is 2,394 and one factor is 798, what is the other factor? ☐

Make up other questions about multiplication.
Ask your partner to display the answers with 0 – 9 tiles.

Teamwork

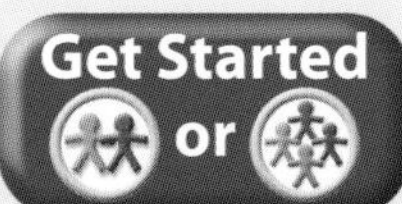

Get paper and a pencil.
Put 1 2 3 4 5 6 7 8 9 in a bag.

Repeat for Each Round

Choose **a, b, c, d, e,** or **f.**
Pick two tiles. Display a two-digit number in the empty squares.
Take turns as you do the steps listed below in order.
Find the number of toys in all. Put the tiles back in the bag.

STEP 1 **Explain how to find the first partial product.**

STEP 2 **Explain how to find the second partial product.**

STEP 3 **Explain how to find the product.**

STEP 4 **Estimate to check that the number of toys in all is reasonable.**

a [ ] [ ] Boxes of toy dogs with 12 dogs in each box

b [ ] [ ] Boxes of toy cats with 24 cats in each box

c [ ] [ ] Boxes of toy dinosaurs with 36 dinosaurs in each box

d [ ] [ ] Boxes of toy cars with 48 cars in each box

e [ ] [ ] Boxes of toy trains with 72 trains in each box

f [ ] [ ] Boxes of toy boats with 96 boats in each box

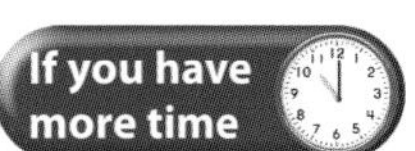

Repeat the activity.

Teamwork

Get 10 squares in one color and 10 in another color.
Get paper and a pencil.
Put 1 2 3 4 5 6 7 8 9 in a bag. Take turns.

Repeat for Each Round

Pick 4 tiles. Display two 2-digit numbers.
Every student multiplies and finds the product.
The student or team that chose the tiles covers the digit in the tens place in the product if it is available on the game board.
Put the tiles back in the bag.

☆ Cover the Digit ☆

6	3	5	9	4
1	7	2	0	8

To win, be the first player or team to cover three digits in the same row.

Play again. This time, cover the digit in the hundreds place in the product.

Think Together

Partner Talk

Share your thinking while you work.

Put 1 2 3 4 in a bag.
Get paper and a pencil.

For Each Round

Choose A, B, C, D, E, or F.
Pick a tile. Pick two tiles if your group has only two students.
Evaluate the expression next to your number.
Discuss: Which three expressions have the same result? Why?
Decide: Which expression has a different result? Why?

A Find the product.	
1	24 × 368
2	12 × 736
3	48 × 184
4	36 × 246

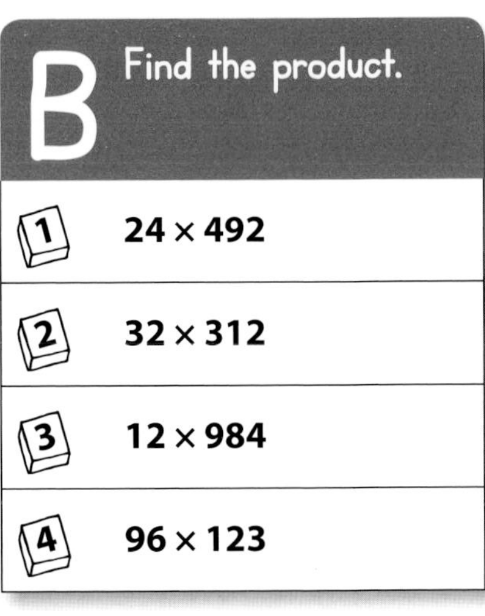

B Find the product.	
1	24 × 492
2	32 × 312
3	12 × 984
4	96 × 123

C Find the product.	
1	38 × 588
2	28 × 756
3	84 × 252
4	42 × 504

D Find the product.	
1	96 × 288
2	32 × 864
3	52 × 532
4	48 × 576

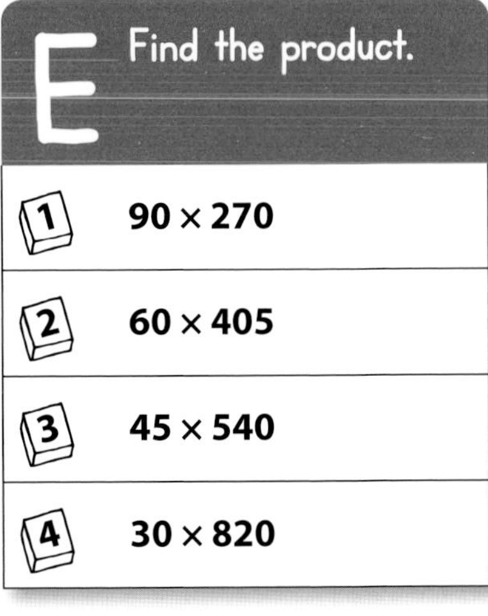

E Find the product.	
1	90 × 270
2	60 × 405
3	45 × 540
4	30 × 820

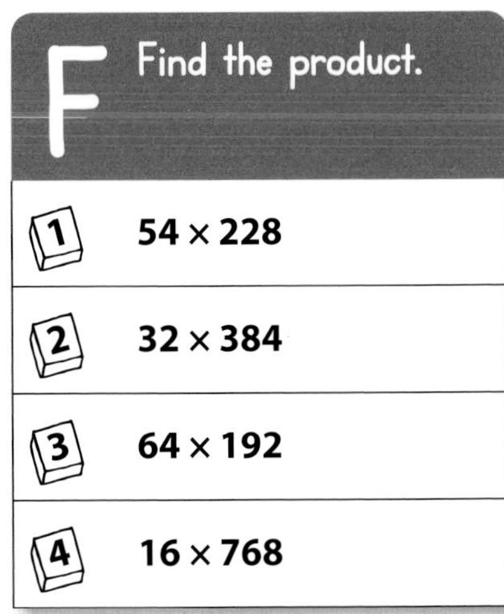

F Find the product.	
1	54 × 228
2	32 × 384
3	64 × 192
4	16 × 768

Make up a "Think Together" question for this multiplication lesson.
Challenge your classmates to think together to answer your question.

Put 1 2 3 4 in a bag.
Get paper and a pencil.

For Each Round

Choose A, B, C, D, E, or **F.**
Pick a tile. Pick two tiles if your group has only two students.
Find the missing factor next to your number.
Discuss: How can estimation help you to find a missing factor?
Decide: Which two-digit factor is the only one that is an odd number?

A

The product is 12,960. Find the missing two-digit factor.

 1	☐☐ × 405
 2	☐☐ × 360
 3	☐☐ × 288
 4	☐☐ × 270

B

The product is 15,552. Find the missing two-digit factor.

 1	☐☐ × 648
 2	☐☐ × 324
 3	☐☐ × 486
 4	☐☐ × 192

C

The product is 16,200. Find the missing two-digit factor.

1	☐☐ × 324
 2	☐☐ × 405
 3	☐☐ × 300
 4	☐☐ × 600

D

The product is 15,120. Find the missing two-digit factor.

 1	☐☐ × 840
 2	☐☐ × 432
 3	☐☐ × 216
 4	☐☐ × 360

E

The product is 5,040. Find the missing two-digit factor.

 1	☐☐ × 240
 2	☐☐ × 360
 3	☐☐ × 120
 4	☐☐ × 180

F

The product is 45,360. Find the missing two-digit factor.

 1	☐☐ × 567
 2	☐☐ × 945
 3	☐☐ × 720
 4	☐☐ × 648

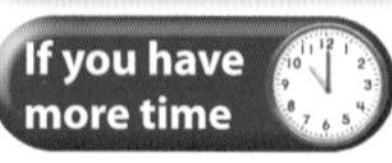

Make up a "Think Together" question for this multiplication lesson.
Challenge your classmates to think together to answer your question.

Display the Digits

0 1 2 3 4 5 6 7 8 9

Pick a tile. Read the problem next to your number. Find the picture that helps you to answer the question. Explain how to answer the question. Cover the picture you chose with your tile. Display each 0 – 9 tile exactly once. If you have a partner, take turns.

A store has a sale, 3 apples for $1. How many apples did Al buy if he paid $9?

Each jar has 27 marbles. How many marbles are in 7 jars?

If you have $7 in quarters, how many quarters do you have?

Tom reads 6 times as many books as Harry. Harry reads 11 books. How many does Tom read?

Susan walks 2 miles in one hour. How far does she walk in 5 hours?

John has 8 times as many apples as Bill. Bill has 3 apples. How many apples does John have?

Each window box has 4 plants. How many plants do 4 window boxes have?

Bill orders 3 pizzas. He pays $12 for each pizza. How much does he spend in all?

Alice earns $15 for every hour she works. How much does Alice make for 5 hours of work?

How many pints do 4 quarts have?

a.
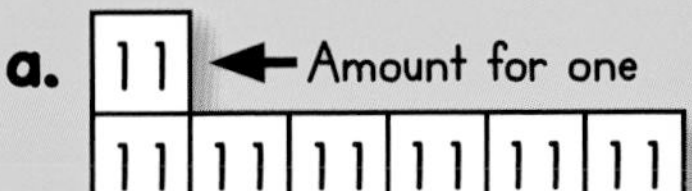

b.
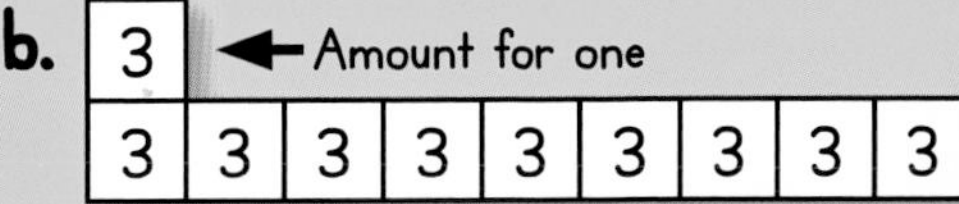

c. 4 ← Amount for one
4 4 4 4

d.
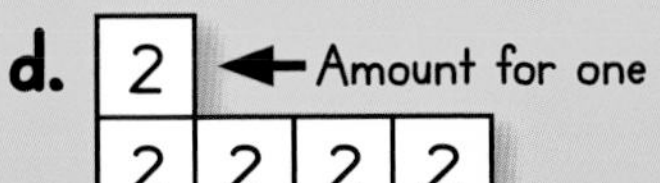

e. 3 ← Amount for one
3 3 3 3 3 3 3 3

f. 12 ← Amount for one
12 12 12

g. 4 ← Amount for one
4 4 4 4 4 4 4

h. 27 ← Amount for one
27 27 27 27 27 27 27

i. 2 ← Amount for one
2 2 2 2 2

j. 15 ← Amount for one
15 15 15 15 15

Make up other questions and pictures like these.
Ask your partner to use your pictures to answer your questions.

Pick a tile. Read the problem next to that tile number. Find the picture that helps you to answer the question. Place your tile next to the picture you choose. Explain how to complete the picture with numbers. Write and solve an equation to answer the question. Display each 0 – 9 tile exactly once. If you have a partner, take turns.

0 How much will 8 window shades cost if each one costs $17?

1 How many inches of ribbon are there in 5 yards?

2 One sidewalk is 14 feet long. How many feet long is a sidewalk that is 9 times as long as the first one?

3 If 36 books fit on a shelf, how many books will fit on 6 shelves?

4 How many hours are there in 5 days?

5 How many apples are in a box that has 4 rows with 7 apples in each row?

6 How many months are there in 8 years?

7 A bag of coffee weighs 1 pound. How many ounces of coffee are in 7 of those bags?

8 If someone earns $250 each week, how much is earned in 4 weeks?

9 What is the total weight of 5 containers that each weigh 56 pounds?

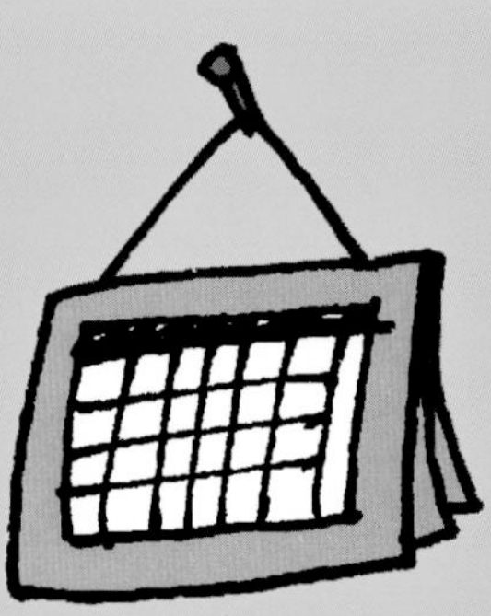

a. ← Amount for one

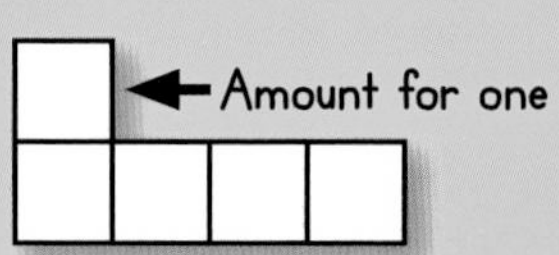

b. ← Amount for one

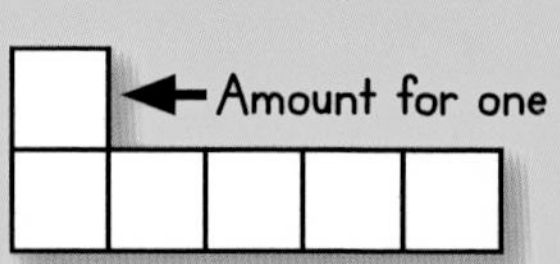

c. ← Amount for one

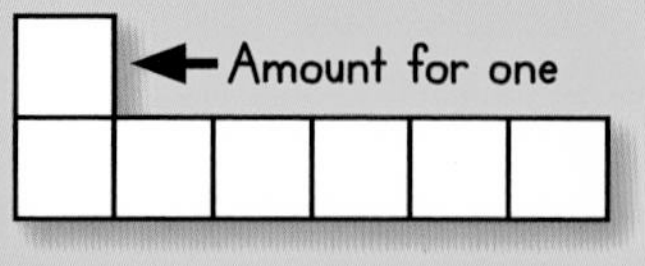

d. ← Amount for one

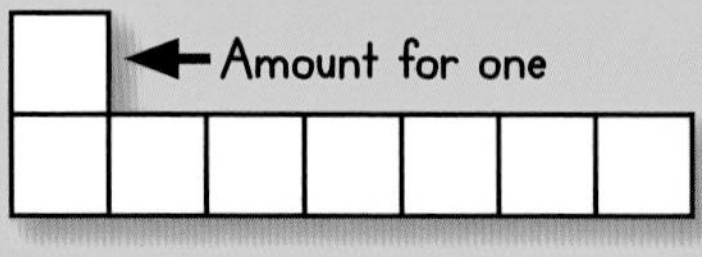

e. ← Amount for one

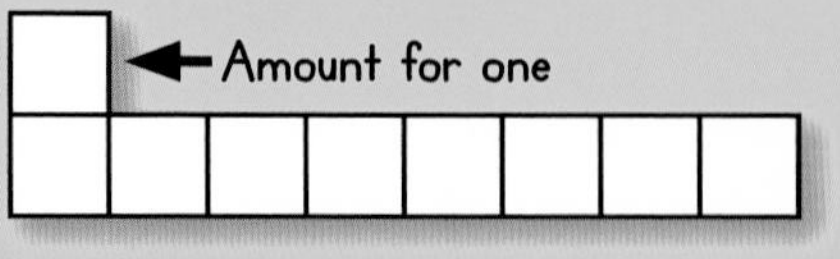

f. ← Amount for one

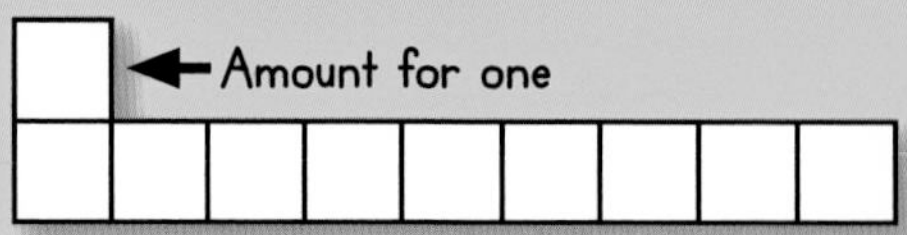

Make up other questions and pictures like these.
Ask your partner to use your pictures to answer your questions.

Get Started Get 10 squares in one color and 10 in another color, two paper clips, and two number cubes. Take turns.

At Your Turn Toss two cubes to find your ovals. **EXAMPLE:** Choose the 3rd oval on the left and the 5th oval on the right, **or** choose the 5th oval on the left and the 3rd oval on the right. Mark your ovals with paper clips.

How to Play Explain how to divide the number on the left by the number on the right. Say a number sentence that includes the quotient. Find and cover the quotient. Lose your turn if the answer is taken.

How to Win The first player or team to get any three connected rectangles in a row or column wins.

Left ovals: 120, 1,200, 24,000, 2,400, 120, 1,200

20	800	4,000	12,000
400	60	600	30
8,000	400	40	200
300	6,000	1,200	600

Right ovals: 2, 3, 6, 4, 3, 6

If you have more time Play again! Talk about how basic facts and patterns can help you to divide.

Get Started  Get 10 squares in one color and 10 in another color, one paper clip, and one number cube. Take turns.

At Your Turn Toss one cube to find your oval. **EXAMPLE:** Choose the 3rd oval on the left, **or** choose the 3rd oval on the right. Mark your oval with a paper clip.

How to Play The number you chose is a quotient. Find the expression that you can compute to get that quotient. Explain how patterns help you to find the quotient. Cover the answer. Lose your turn if the answer is taken.

How to Win The first player or team to get any three connected rectangles in a row or column wins.

Left ovals: 700, 80, 9,000, 7,000, 600, 60

5,600 ÷ 8	54,000 ÷ 6	720 ÷ 8	7,200 ÷ 8
49,000 ÷ 7	36,000 ÷ 6	4,800 ÷ 6	630 ÷ 9
5,600 ÷ 7	6,300 ÷ 7	560 ÷ 7	81,000 ÷ 9
64,000 ÷ 8	540 ÷ 9	42,000 ÷ 6	5,400 ÷ 9

Right ovals: 6,000, 900, 70, 90, 800, 8,000

 **If you have more time** Play again! Talk about your strategies as you play.

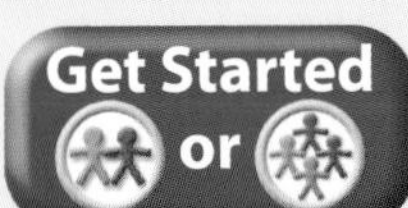

Put 1 2 3 4 in a bag.

For Each Round

Choose A, B, C, D, E, or F.
Pick a tile. Pick two tiles if your group has only two students.
Evaluate the expression next to your number.
Discuss: Which three expressions have the same estimate? Why?
Decide: Which expression has a different estimate? Why?

A Round the dividend to the nearest hundred. Estimate the quotient.

1	378 ÷ 4
2	429 ÷ 4
3	474 ÷ 4
4	362 ÷ 4

B Use compatible numbers to estimate each quotient.

1	537 ÷ 6
2	713 ÷ 8
3	349 ÷ 4
4	339 ÷ 7

C Round the dividend to the nearest hundred. Estimate the quotient.

1	583 ÷ 2
2	525 ÷ 2
3	639 ÷ 2
4	608 ÷ 2

D Use compatible numbers to estimate each quotient.

1	189 ÷ 4
2	411 ÷ 8
3	233 ÷ 6
4	347 ÷ 7

E Round the dividend to the nearest hundred. Estimate the quotient.

1	441 ÷ 5
2	487 ÷ 5
3	542 ÷ 5
4	539 ÷ 5

F Use compatible numbers to estimate each quotient.

1	348 ÷ 9
2	351 ÷ 6
3	198 ÷ 5
4	291 ÷ 7

Make up a "Think Together" question for this lesson.
Challenge your classmates to think together to answer your question.

Put 1 2 3 4 in a bag.

For Each Round

Choose A or B.
Pick a tile. Pick two tiles if your group has only two students.
Ask a question. Follow the directions next to your number.
Discuss: How did your group members estimate?
Decide: Does every group member have a reasonable estimate?

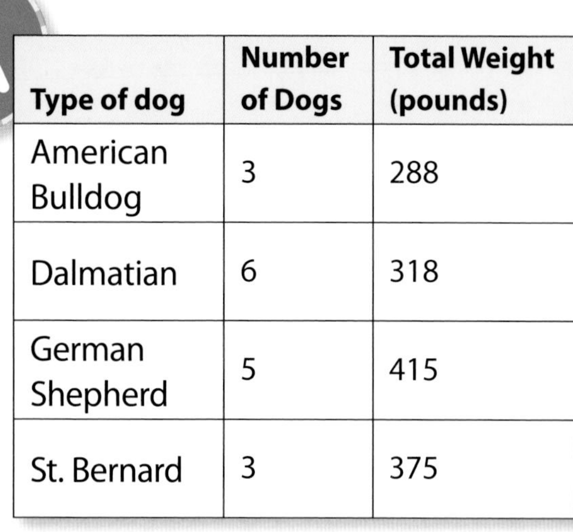

A

Type of dog	Number of Dogs	Total Weight (pounds)
American Bulldog	3	288
Dalmatian	6	318
German Shepherd	5	415
St. Bernard	3	375

B

Family	Hours Driven	Total Miles
Clark	7	341
Gilbert	9	522
Hernandez	3	178
Nicolosi	8	346

Do These Steps in Order

1. **Ask a question about the data so that your group can estimate a quotient.**

2. **Ask a different question about the data so that your group can estimate a quotient.**

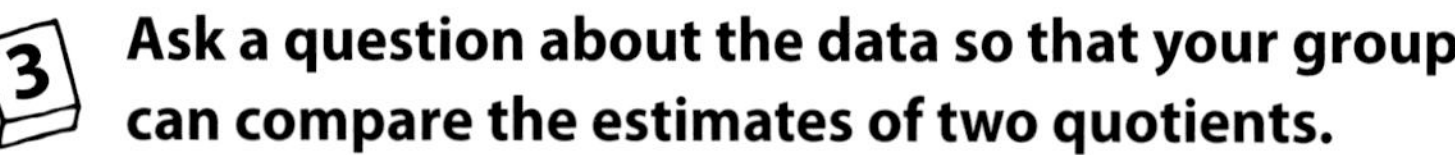

3. **Ask a question about the data so that your group can compare the estimates of two quotients.**

4. **Ask another question about the data so that your group can determine if a number is an overestimate or an underestimate.**

Repeat the activity using data not previously discussed.

Display the Digits

0 1 2 3 4 5 6 7 8 9

Read a question. Explain how to answer the question.
Make sure your answer is reasonable. Display each 0 – 9 tile exactly once.
If you have a partner, take turns.

a. Saul has 35 daisies. He can plant 4 daisies in each pot. How many pots can he completely fill? ☐

How many daisies does Saul have left after filling complete pots? ☐

b. Betty's class is going on a field trip. 22 students will go. If 5 students can fit in a car, how many full cars will go? ☐

How many students in Betty's class will ride in a car that isn't full? ☐

c. Mike can fit 6 baseball cards to a page. He has 65 cards. How many pages can he fill? ☐☐

How many cards does Mike have left? ☐

d. Arnelle bought 127 apples for her class. There are 20 students, including Arnelle. How many apples can each student get? ☐

How many apples does Arnelle have left after 20 students share 127 apples equally? ☐

e. Each package of dog treats has 6 treats. If Carl's dog eats 1 treat a day, how many boxes does Carl need to buy for a 50-day supply? ☐

Make up other questions like these.
Ask your partner to display the answers with 0 – 9 tiles.

Read a question. Explain how to answer the question.
Make sure your answer is reasonable. Display each 0 – 9 tile exactly once.
If you have a partner, take turns.

a. Lanny has 45 baseball cards. Only 6 cards fit on a page in his scrapbook. How many pages of baseball cards will be in his scrapbook? ☐

If Lanny fills as many pages as possible, how many baseball cards will be on the last page? ☐

b. Ms. Jones is throwing a party for her students. She has 53 students. How many student tables will be needed if 6 students can fit at a table? ☐

Ms. Jones will fill as many tables as possible, and then sit at the table which is partially filled. How many students will be seated with her? ☐

c. Leigh Ann baked 24 cookies. She then separated them into bags with a dozen cookies per bag. How many bags does she need in all? ☐

How many bags of cookies will be partially filled? ☐

d. Scarves normally cost $9 each. Erica found them on special offer: "three scarves for $25." Erica needs to buy 6 scarves for her friends. How many dollars will she save using this special offer? ☐

If Erica decides to buy 9 scarves at the special price, how many dollars will she save? ☐

e. Faisal and 84 other fifth grade students are going on a field trip. Each car holds 5 students. How many cars are needed? ☐☐

Make up other questions like these.
Ask your partner to display the answers with 0 – 9 tiles.

Get Started 

Get 10 squares in one color and 10 in another color.
Get two number cubes. Take turns with another player or team.
Talk about math as you play!

At Your Turn

Toss two number cubes. Add the dots. Find your toss below.
Follow the directions. Explain your thinking. Cover the answer.
If the answer is taken, lose your turn. Have fun!

Toss	How much money is shown? Explain how to divide the money equally among that number of people. Find and say a division number sentence that shows how you shared the money.	
2	100 10 10 1 1 1 1 1 1	9 people
3	100 100 100 10 1 1	6 people
4	100 10 10 10 10 1 1 1 1 1 1 1	7 people
5	100 100 10 10 10 10 10 1 1 1 1 1	5 people
6	100 10 10 10 10 10 10 1 1 1 1	4 people
7	100 10 10 10 10 10 10 10 10 1 1	2 people
8	100 10 10 10 10 10 1 1 1	3 people
9	100 100 100 10 10 1 1 1 1	4 people
10	100 100 10 10 10 10 1 1 1 1 1 1	6 people
11	100 100 10 10 1 1 1 1 1	5 people
12	100 10 10 10 10 1 1 1 1	8 people

$324 ÷ 4 = $81	$225 ÷ 5 = $45	$153 ÷ 3 = $51	$126 ÷ 9 = $14
$144 ÷ 8 = $18	$182 ÷ 2 = $91	$255 ÷ 5 = $51	$164 ÷ 4 = $41
$164 ÷ 4 = $41	$246 ÷ 6 = $41	$312 ÷ 6 = $52	$324 ÷ 4 = $81
$255 ÷ 5 = $51	$153 ÷ 3 = $51	$182 ÷ 2 = $91	$147 ÷ 7 = $21

How to Win

You win if you are the first to get four connected rectangles, like:

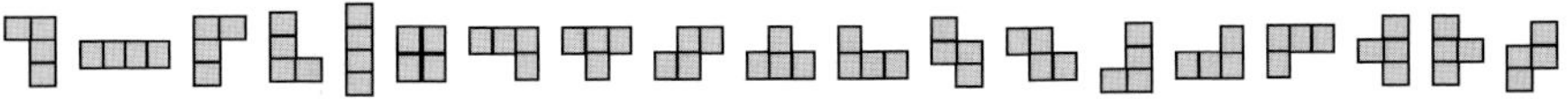

Play again!

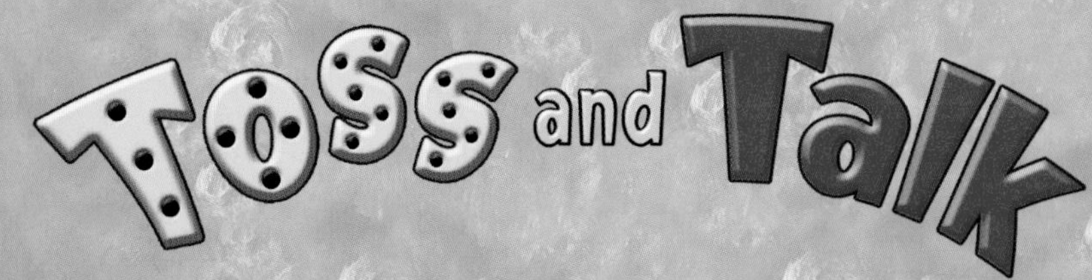

Get 10 squares in one color and 10 in another color.
Get two number cubes. Take turns with another player or team.
Talk about math as you play!

At Your Turn

Toss two number cubes. Add the dots. Find your toss below.
Follow the directions. Explain your thinking. Cover the answer.
If the answer is taken, lose your turn. Have fun!

Toss	Explain how the people can share hundred-dollar bills, ten-dollar bills, and one-dollar bills so that each person gets the same amount of money.
2	If 9 people share $126 equally, how much money does each person get?
3	If 6 people share $312 equally, how much money does each person get?
4	If 7 people share $147 equally, how much money does each person get?
5	If 5 people share $245 equally, how much money does each person get?
6	If 4 people share $160 equally, how much money does each person get?
7	If 2 people share $182 equally, how much money does each person get?
8	If 3 people share $153 equally, how much money does each person get?
9	If 4 people share $324 equally, how much money does each person get?
10	If 6 people share $246 equally, how much money does each person get?
11	If 5 people share $225 equally, how much money does each person get?
12	If 8 people share $144 equally, how much money does each person get?

$81	$45	$51	$14
$18	$91	$49	$40
$40	$41	$52	$81
$49	$51	$91	$21

How to Win

You win if you are the first to get four connected rectangles, like:

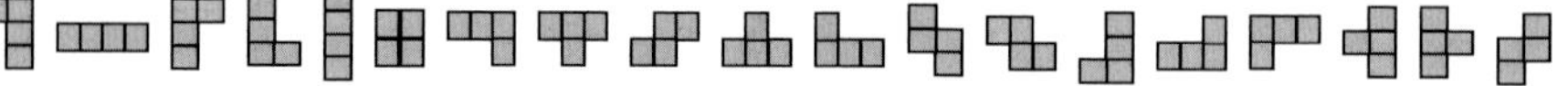

Play again!

Quick Questions

Get Started 

Each player tosses two number cubes.
If your numbers match another player's numbers, toss again.
Decide who will read the first question. Take turns.

For Each Question

Listen to the reader. You may use mental math or paper and a pencil. Discuss and agree on the correct answer. Every player who has that answer can remove <u>one</u> cube that shows the answer.

How to Win

The first player who removes both cubes wins. Have fun!

a	Find the quotient for $6\overline{)380}$. Which digit is in the tens place?
b	Find the quotient for $5\overline{)271}$. Which digit is in the ones place?
c	Find the quotient for $7\overline{)153}$. Which digit is in the tens place?
d	Find the quotient for $6\overline{)370}$. Which digit is in the ones place?
e	Find the quotient for $7\overline{)374}$. Which digit is in the tens place?
f	Find the quotient for $9\overline{)438}$. Which digit is in the tens place?
g	Find the quotient for $2\overline{)187}$. Which digit is in the ones place?
h	Find the quotient for $8\overline{)437}$. Which digit is in the ones place?
i	Find the quotient for $4\overline{)215}$. Which digit is in the ones place?
j	Find the quotient for $4\overline{)254}$. Which digit is in the tens place?
k	Find the quotient for $2\overline{)143}$. Which digit is in the ones place?
l	Find the quotient for $8\overline{)413}$. Which digit is in the tens place?
m	Find the quotient for $9\overline{)618}$. Which digit is in the tens place?

n	Find the quotient for $3\overline{)283}$. Which digit is in the ones place?
o	Find the quotient for $3\overline{)278}$. Which digit is in the ones place?
p	Find the quotient for $6\overline{)191}$. Which digit is in the tens place?
q	Find the quotient for $5\overline{)156}$. Which digit is in the ones place?
r	Find the quotient for $6\overline{)490}$. Which digit is in the ones place?
s	Find the quotient for $2\overline{)123}$. Which digit is in the tens place?
t	Find the quotient for $3\overline{)164}$. Which digit is in the ones place?
u	Find the quotient for $8\overline{)659}$. Which digit is in the ones place?
v	Find the quotient for $5\overline{)277}$. Which digit is in the tens place?
w	Find the quotient for $9\overline{)375}$. Which digit is in the tens place?
x	Find the quotient for $3\overline{)157}$. Which digit is in the ones place?
y	Find the quotient for $4\overline{)159}$. Which digit is in the tens place?
z	Find the quotient for $7\overline{)222}$. Which digit is in the ones place?

Toss two number cubes again. Play another game.
Begin with the next question in the list.

Quick Questions

Each player tosses two number cubes.
If your numbers match another player's numbers, toss again.
Decide who will read the first question. Take turns.

For Each Question

Listen to the reader. You may use mental math or paper and a pencil. Discuss and agree on the correct answer. Every player who has that answer can remove one cube that shows the answer.

How to Win

The first player who removes both cubes wins. Have fun!

a	Find the quotient for 6)380. What is the remainder?
b	Find the quotient for 5)271. Which digit is in the ones place?
c	Find the quotient for 7)153. What is the remainder?
d	Find the quotient for 6)370. Which digit is in the ones place?
e	Find the quotient for 7)374. What is the remainder?
f	Find the quotient for 9)438. What is the remainder?
g	Find the quotient for 2)187. Which digit is in the ones place?
h	Find the quotient for 8)437. What is the remainder?
i	Find the quotient for 4)215. Which digit is in the ones place?
j	Find the quotient for 4)254. What is the remainder?
k	Find the quotient for 2)143. What is the remainder?
l	Find the quotient for 8)413. What is the remainder?
m	Find the quotient for 9)618. What is the remainder?

n	Find the quotient for 3)283. Which digit is in the ones place?
o	Find the quotient for 3)278. Which digit is in the ones place?
p	Find the quotient for 6)191. What is the remainder?
q	Find the quotient for 5)156. Which digit is in the ones place?
r	Find the quotient for 6)490. What is the remainder?
s	Find the quotient for 2)123. What is the remainder?
t	Find the quotient for 3)164. What is the remainder?
u	Find the quotient for 8)659. What is the remainder?
v	Find the quotient for 5)277. Which digit is in the ones place?
w	Find the quotient for 9)375. What is the remainder?
x	Find the quotient for 3)157. Which digit is in the ones place?
y	Find the quotient for 4)159. What is the remainder?
z	Find the quotient for 7)222. What is the remainder?

Play another game. Begin with the next question in the list. Or make up your own questions like these. Play the game with your questions.

Display the Digits

0 1 2 3 4 5 6 7 8 9

Explain how to find the quotient. Use mental math or paper and a pencil. Display each 0 – 9 tile exactly once. If you have a partner, take turns.

a. Divide 627 by 3. What is the digit in the hundreds place in the quotient?

b. Divide 824 by 8. What is the digit in the ones place in the quotient?

c. Divide 605 by 4. What is the digit in the tens place in the quotient?

d. Divide 627 by 3. What is the digit in the ones place in the quotient?

e. Divide 832 by 4. What is the digit in the ones place in the quotient?

f. Divide 600 by 4. What is the digit in the hundreds place in the quotient?

g. Divide 627 by 3. What is the digit in the tens place in the quotient?

h. Divide 602 by 7. What is the digit in the ones place in the quotient?

i. Divide 642 by 6. What is the digit in the ones place in the quotient?

j. Divide 608 by 2. What is the digit in the ones place in the quotient?

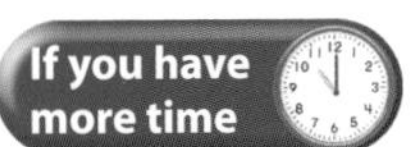

Make up other questions like these.
Ask your partner to display the answers with 0 – 9 tiles.

Display the Digits

0 1 2 3 4 5 6 7 8 9

Read what is given. Explain how to find the quotient and the remainder. Use mental math or paper and a pencil. Display each 0 – 9 tile exactly once. If you have a partner, take turns.

a. Divide 625 by 3. What is the remainder? ☐

b. Divide 628 by 6. What is the remainder? ☐

c. Divide 621 by 3. What is the remainder? ☐

d. Divide 627 by 3. What digit is in the ones place in the quotient? ☐

e. Divide 547 by 5. What is the remainder? ☐

f. Divide 636 by 7. What is the remainder? ☐

g. Divide 407 by 4. What is the remainder? ☐

h. Divide 832 by 4. What digit is in the ones place in the quotient? ☐

i. Divide 285 by 7. What is the remainder? ☐

j. Divide 647 by 8. What is the remainder? ☐

Make up other questions like these.
Ask your partner to display the answers with 0 – 9 tiles.

Teamwork

Get paper and a pencil.
Put 1 2 3 4 in a bag.

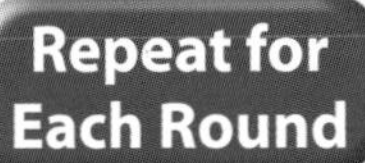

Choose **a** or **b**. Ask someone to read the problem aloud.
Pick a tile. Pick two tiles if your group has only two students.
Do the jobs listed below in order. To find your job, find the number that matches the tile you chose.

Draw a picture for the problem.

Write an equation.

Explain how to solve the equation written in step 2.

Answer the question. Explain the answer.
Is it reasonable? Why?

a. The fifth-grade class at Hawthorne School collected empty two-liter bottles and put them into cartons. If they collected 65 bottles and each carton holds 12 bottles, how many cartons did they fill? How many bottles were left over?

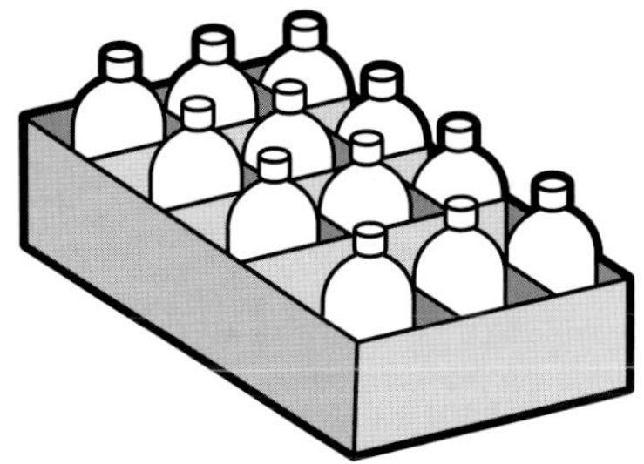

b. Maria's father drives 240 miles to work and back every two weeks. He drives 20 miles each day. How many days per week does he work?

Choose **a** or **b**. Change the two numbers in the problem and solve the problem again.

Teamwork

Get Started

Get paper and a pencil.
Put 1 2 3 4 in a bag.

Repeat for Each Round

Choose **a** or **b**.
Pick a tile. Pick two tiles if your group has only two students.
Do the jobs listed below in order. To find your job, find the number that matches the tile you chose.

 **Draw a picture for the problem.**

 **Write an equation.**

 **Explain how to solve the equation written in step 2.**

 **Answer the question. Explain the answer. Is it reasonable? Why?**

a. Emerson School is taking all of its fifth-graders and teachers on a field trip. There are 62 fifth-grade students and four teachers. If each minibus holds 18 people, how many mini buses will be needed for the trip?

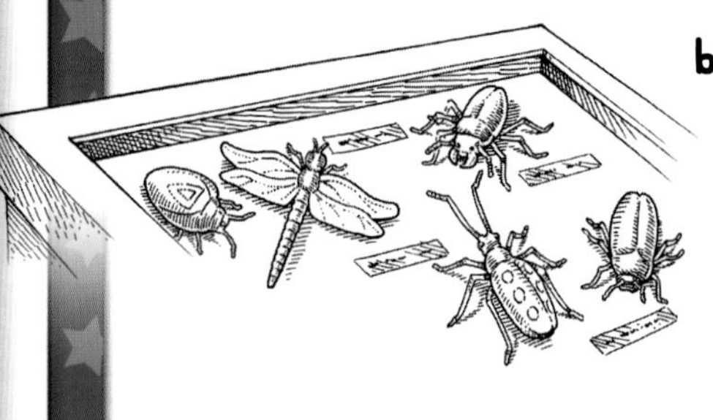

b. Emile collects insects which he wants to display on padded boards using a pin. He has four boards and he has collected 53 insects. Can he display the same number of insects on each board? If so, how many would be on each board? If not, how many more insects would he need to have the same number on each board?

Choose **a** or **b**. Change the two numbers in the problem and solve the problem again.

Get Started  Get 10 squares in one color and 10 in another color, two paper clips, and two number cubes. Take turns.

At Your Turn Toss two cubes to find your ovals. **EXAMPLE:** [3] [5] Choose the 3rd oval on the left and the 5th oval on the right, **or** choose the 5th oval on the left and the 3rd oval on the right. Mark your ovals with paper clips.

How to Play Divide the number on the left by the number on the right. Explain how to use patterns to divide. Find and cover the quotient. Lose your turn if the answer is taken.

How to Win The first player or team to get any three connected rectangles in a row or column wins.

Left ovals					Right ovals
2,400	80	8	4	40	30
1,200	400	60	30	300	40
240	200	20	40	600	60
12,000	60	12	6	120	20
1,200					60
240					40

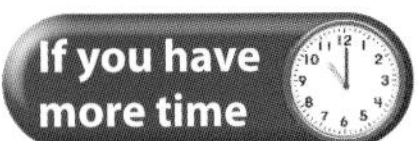

Play again! Talk about how you use patterns to divide.

Get Started  Get 10 squares in one color and 10 in another color, one paper clip, and one number cube. Take turns.

At Your Turn Toss the cube to find your oval. **EXAMPLE:** Choose the 3rd oval on the left, **or** choose the 3rd oval on the right. Mark your oval with a paper clip.

How to Play The number you chose is a quotient. Find the expression that you can compute to get that quotient. Explain how patterns can help you to divide. Find and cover the answer. Lose your turn if the answer is taken.

How to Win The first player or team to get any three connected rectangles in a row or column wins.

Left ovals: 60, 50, 100, 30, 40, 300

1,500 ÷ 30	1,800 ÷ 30	3,600 ÷ 60	1,800 ÷ 60
6,400 ÷ 80	1,800 ÷ 90	3,000 ÷ 30	2,800 ÷ 40
5,400 ÷ 60	2,400 ÷ 60	5,600 ÷ 80	3,500 ÷ 70
1,500 ÷ 50	27,000 ÷ 90	200 ÷ 20	10,000 ÷ 50

Right ovals: 20, 80, 70, 90, 10, 200

Play again! Talk about your strategies as you play.

Get 10 squares in one color and 10 in another color.
Get two number cubes. Take turns with another player or team.
Talk about math as you play!

At Your Turn

Toss two number cubes. Add the dots. Find your toss below.
Follow the directions. Explain your thinking. Cover the answer.
If the answer is taken, lose your turn. Have fun!

Toss	Find two compatible numbers you can use to estimate the quotient. Explain, and then say the estimated quotient.
2	389 ÷ 25
3	274 ÷ 33
4	2,820 ÷ 43
5	375 ÷ 12
6	6,890 ÷ 56
7	3,234 ÷ 78
8	2,235 ÷ 64
9	791 ÷ 79
10	2,819 ÷ 69
11	485 ÷ 68
12	267 ÷ 89

2,100 ÷ 70	490 ÷ 70	270 ÷ 90	2,800 ÷ 70
300 ÷ 10	700 ÷ 70	270 ÷ 30	2,800 ÷ 40
800 ÷ 80	2,800 ÷ 70	400 ÷ 25	6,000 ÷ 50
1,800 ÷ 60	6,000 ÷ 60	3,200 ÷ 80	360 ÷ 12

You win if you are the first to get four connected rectangles, like:

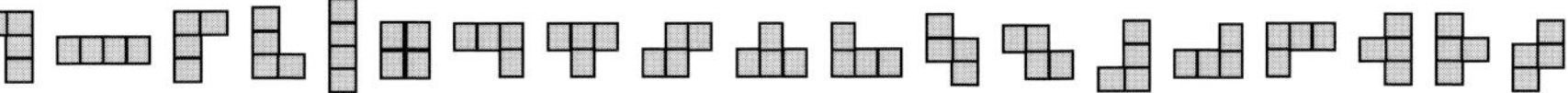

Play again!

Get Started 

Get 10 squares in one color and 10 in another color.
Get two number cubes. Take turns with another player or team.
Talk about math as you play!

At Your Turn

Toss two number cubes. Add the dots. Find your toss below.
Follow the directions. Explain your thinking. Cover the answer.
If the answer is taken, lose your turn. Have fun!

Toss	For which dividend and divisor would these compatible numbers help you to estimate the quotient? Explain.
2	320 ÷ 80
3	700 ÷ 70
4	480 ÷ 80
5	800 ÷ 80
6	350 ÷ 70
7	560 ÷ 70
8	420 ÷ 60
9	630 ÷ 90
10	240 ÷ 80
11	270 ÷ 30
12	280 ÷ 40

325 ÷ 78	400 ÷ 57	565 ÷ 65	440 ÷ 62
777 ÷ 76	584 ÷ 67	727 ÷ 73	275 ÷ 37
229 ÷ 75	490 ÷ 78	689 ÷ 92	274 ÷ 29
650 ÷ 87	363 ÷ 69	791 ÷ 79	351 ÷ 72

How to Win

You win if you are the first to get four connected rectangles, like:

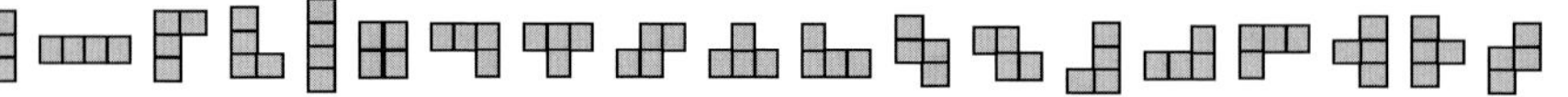

If you have more time

Play again!

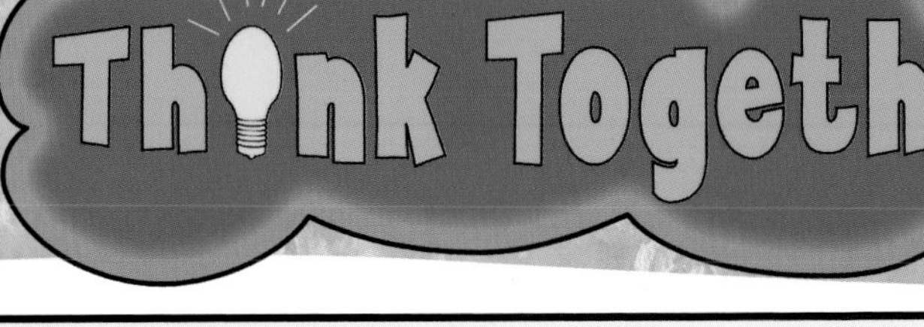

Think Together

Partner Talk

Share your thinking while you work.

Get Started

Put 1 2 3 4 in a bag.

For Each Round

Choose A, B, C, D, E, or F.

Pick a tile. Pick two tiles if your group has only two students.

Evaluate the expression. Use the value of the variable next to your tile number.

Discuss: How does the value of the expression change as the value of the variable increases? Why?

A Evaluate the expression: $\frac{50}{n}$

	$n = 2$
	$n = 3$
	$n = 4$
	$n = 5$

B Evaluate the expression: $41.2 - n$

	$n = 2$
	$n = 3$
	$n = 4$
	$n = 5$

C Evaluate the expression: $\frac{n}{3}$

	$n = 2$
	$n = 3$
	$n = 4$
	$n = 5$

D Evaluate the expression: $14n$

	$n = 2$
	$n = 3$
	$n = 4$
	$n = 5$

E Evaluate the expression: $7.8 + n$

	 $n = 2$
	$n = 3$
	$n = 4$
	$n = 5$

F Evaluate the expression: $n \times 25$

	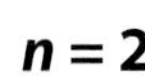 $n = 2$
	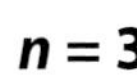 $n = 3$
	$n = 4$
	$n = 5$

Make up an expression with a variable. Challenge your group to think together to evaluate your expression for $n = 2$, $n = 3$, $n = 4$, and $n = 5$.

Put 1 2 3 4 in a bag.

For Each Round

Choose A, B, C, D, E, or F.
Pick a tile. Pick two tiles if your group has only two students.
Evaluate the expression for the value of the variable next to your number.
Discuss: Compare the results for $n = 5$ and $n = 10$, or $n = 6$ and $n = 12$.
Decide: Do you notice a pattern? Can you explain it?

A Evaluate the expression: $3n + 4$

1	$n = 5$
2	$n = 6$
3	$n = 10$
4	$n = 12$

B Evaluate the expression: $n \times n$

1	$n = 5$
2	$n = 6$
3	$n = 10$
4	$n = 12$

C Evaluate the expression: $\frac{120}{n}$

1	$n = 5$
2	$n = 6$
3	$n = 10$
4	$n = 12$

D Evaluate the expression: $10n - 10$

1	$n = 5$
2	$n = 6$
3	$n = 10$
4	$n = 12$

E Evaluate the expression: $2.5n$

1	$n = 5$
2	$n = 6$
3	$n = 10$
4	$n = 12$

F Evaluate the expression: $\frac{n}{0.5}$

1	$n = 5$
2	$n = 6$
3	$n = 10$
4	$n = 12$

Make up an expression with a variable. Challenge your group to think together to evaluate your expression for $n = 2$, $n = 3$, $n = 4$, and $n = 5$.

Display the Digits

0 1 2 3 4 5 6 7 8 9

Use paper and a pencil to divide. Explain your steps. Find the missing digit in each quotient. Display each 0 – 9 tile exactly once. If you have a partner, take turns.

a. 216 ÷ 30 = ☐ R 6

b. 807 ÷ 80 = 1☐ R 7

c. 639 ÷ 70 = ☐ R 9

d. 85 ÷ 40 = ☐ R 5

e. 159 ÷ 50 = ☐ R 9

f. 371 ÷ 60 = ☐ R 11

g. 48 ÷ 40 = ☐ R 8

h. 345 ÷ 80 = ☐ R 25

i. 467 ÷ 90 = ☐ R 17

j. 168 ÷ 20 = ☐ R 8

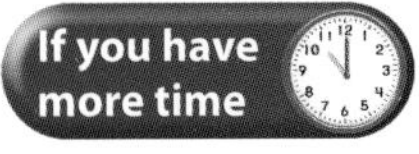

Make up other division puzzles like these.
Ask your partner to display the answers with 0 – 9 tiles.

Display the Digits

0 1 2 3 4 5 6 7 8 9

Explain how to find the missing digits.
Display each 0 – 9 tile exactly once. If you have a partner, take turns.

```
       2 7 R 4
 [a] 0)8 [b] 4
     - 6 0
      [c] 1 4
     - 2 1 [d]
           [e]
```

```
         1 2 R 15
 80)[f] [g] [h]
  - [i] 0
     1 7 5
  - 1 [j] 0
       1 5
```

a	b	c	d	e
f	g	h	i	j

Make up other division puzzles like these.
Ask your partner to display the answers with 0 – 9 tiles.

Teamwork

Get Started 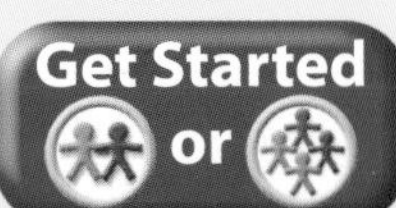

Get paper and a pencil.
Get 0 1 2 3 4 5 6 7 8 9.

Repeat for Each Round

Choose **a, b, c, d, e, f, g, h, i,** or **j**.
Take turns as you do each step. Explain your thinking.

STEP 1
Explain how to estimate the quotient.

STEP 2
Explain how to find the quotient.

STEP 3
Find the remainder and check that it is less than the divisor.

STEP 4
Check the answer. Display a tile for the 1-digit quotient.

a. $332 \div 42 = \square$

b. $294 \div 47 = \square$

c. $277 \div 34 = \square$

d. $281 \div 29 = \square$

e. $193 \div 96 = \square$

f. $295 \div 97 = \square$

g. $423 \div 86 = \square$

h. $382 \div 76 = \square$

i. $0 \div 67 = \square$

j. $123 \div 92 = \square$

When you have completed all ten rounds correctly, each 0 – 9 tile will be displayed exactly once.

Pick any number tile. Divide a three-digit dividend by a two-digit divisor to get that number as the quotient.

Teamwork

Get paper and a pencil.
Put 1 2 3 4 in a bag.

Repeat for Each Round

Choose **a, b, c, d, e, f, g,** or **h**.
Pick a tile. Pick two tiles if your group has only two students.
Do the jobs listed below in order.
To find your job, find the number that matches the tile you chose.

 **Explain how to estimate the quotient.**

 **Explain how to adjust the estimated quotient if necessary. Find the quotient and the remainder.**

 **Check. Multiply the quotient by the divisor and add the remainder.**

 **Try this challenge: Explain how to adjust the dividend so that when you divide the adjusted dividend by the divisor, the remainder is 0.**

a.	$231 \div 29$	**b.**	$634 \div 78$
c.	$423 \div 86$	**d.**	$230 \div 56$
e.	$295 \div 97$	**f.**	$227 \div 42$
g.	$578 \div 64$	**h.**	$238 \div 39$

Choose your own two-digit divisor and any three-digit dividend.
Repeat steps 1 – 4 for your numbers.

Tic Tac Toe

Get Started 

Get 20 squares in one color and 20 in another color. Get two number cubes for players to share. Get paper and a pencil. Take turns.

For Each Round

Toss one cube. That is the number of tens in a two-digit divisor. Toss the other cube. That is the number of ones in the same two-digit divisor. Explain how to divide 792 by that two-digit divisor. Cover the answer. If the answer is taken, lose your turn.

Example

← 3 tens 5 ones

```
    22 R 22
35 )792
    70
     92
     70
     22
```

Divide 792 by the two-digit divisor!

How to Win

The first player or team to cover a row, column, or diagonal in one of the four sections of the game board wins.

37 R 15	15 R 27	31 R 17	17 R 27	49 R 8	24 R 0
14 R 8	72 R 0	14 R 22	34 R 10	12 R 0	12 R 36
22 R 0	14 R 36	24 R 24	18 R 0	12 R 60	12 R 48
60 R 12	12 R 12	56 R 8	15 R 12	66 R 0	19 R 13
33 R 0	25 R 17	12 R 24	36 R 0	52 R 12	30 R 12
18 R 36	22 R 22	18 R 18	17 R 10	14 R 50	23 R 10

If you have more time Play again!

Tic Tac Toe

Get Started 
Get 20 squares in one color and 20 in another color. Get two number cubes for players to share. Get paper and a pencil. Take turns.

For Each Round
Toss two cubes. Make either number the number of tens in a two-digit divisor. Make the other number the number of ones in the same two-digit divisor. Find the dividend and the quotient with that number as the missing divisor. Explain your answer. Cover the answer. If the answer is taken, lose your turn.

Find the missing divisor!

Example
3 tens 5 ones or 5 tens 3 ones
Choose a divisor of 35 or 53.
Use estimation to help you place that divisor below. Multiply to check.

How to Win
The first player or team to cover a row, column, or diagonal in one of the four sections of the game board wins.

14 R 14 □ □)924	71 R 1 □ □)924	15 R 9 □ □)924	66 R 0 □ □)924	40 R 4 □ □)924	17 R 6 □ □)924
14 R 0 □ □)924	16 R 28 □ □)924	35 R 14 □ □)924	27 R 6 □ □)924	17 R 23 □ □)924	38 R 12 □ □)924
14 R 56 □ □)924	21 R 21 □ □)924	14 R 28 □ □)924	44 R 0 □ □)924	17 R 40 □ □)924	21 R 0 □ □)924
42 R 0 □ □)924	14 R 42 □ □)924	29 R 25 □ □)924	84 R 0 □ □)924	57 R 12 □ □)924	26 R 14 □ □)924
20 R 24 □ □)924	77 R 0 □ □)924	22 R 22 □ □)924	61 R 9 □ □)924	25 R 24 □ □)924	36 R 24 □ □)924
16 R 44 □ □)924	28 R 0 □ □)924	18 R 6 □ □)924	28 R 28 □ □)924	22 R 0 □ □)924	20 R 4 □ □)924

Play again!

Quick Questions

Center Activity **5-7** ★

Get Started or or

Get one calculator. Each player tosses two number cubes. If your numbers match another player's numbers, toss again. Decide who will read the first question. Take turns.

For Each Question

Listen to the reader. Discuss and agree on an estimate. Ask one student to use a calculator to find the quotient. That student rounds the quotient to the nearest whole number if necessary, and then reads the quotient. Every player who has the digit in the hundreds place in the quotient can remove one cube that shows the answer.

How to Win

The first player who removes both cubes wins. Have fun!

a	Divide 6,591 by 42. The quotient has which digit in the hundreds place?
b	Divide 8,825 by 14. The quotient has which digit in the hundreds place?
c	Divide 9,161 by 81. The quotient has which digit in the hundreds place?
d	Divide 8,626 by 27. The quotient has which digit in the hundreds place?
e	Divide 5,637 by 11. The quotient has which digit in the hundreds place?
f	Divide 8,966 by 36. The quotient has which digit in the hundreds place?
g	Divide 8,418 by 18. The quotient has which digit in the hundreds place?
h	Divide 9,959 by 23. The quotient has which digit in the hundreds place?
i	Divide 6,693 by 23. The quotient has which digit in the hundreds place?
j	Divide 8,168 by 16. The quotient has which digit in the hundreds place?
k	Divide 7,979 by 39. The quotient has which digit in the hundreds place?
l	Divide 9,651 by 16. The quotient has which digit in the hundreds place?
m	Divide 9,389 by 24. The quotient has which digit in the hundreds place?

n	Divide 9,547 by 29. The quotient has which digit in the hundreds place?
o	Divide 7,040 by 16. The quotient has which digit in the hundreds place?
p	Divide 8,773 by 68. The quotient has which digit in the hundreds place?
q	Divide 6,318 by 12. The quotient has which digit in the hundreds place?
r	Divide 5,222 by 14. The quotient has which digit in the hundreds place?
s	Divide 9,345 by 15. The quotient has which digit in the hundreds place?
t	Divide 8,458 by 72. The quotient has which digit in the hundreds place?
u	Divide 5,980 by 14. The quotient has which digit in the hundreds place?
v	Divide 7,594 by 37. The quotient has which digit in the hundreds place?
w	Divide 4,346 by 12. The quotient has which digit in the hundreds place?
x	Divide 7,723 by 13. The quotient has which digit in the hundreds place?
y	Divide 8,895 by 14. The quotient has which digit in the hundreds place?
z	Divide 5,797 by 25. The quotient has which digit in the hundreds place?

Toss two number cubes again. Play another game. Begin with the next question in the list.

Quick Questions

Get one calculator. Each player tosses two number cubes. If your numbers match another player's numbers, toss again. Decide who will read the first question. Take turns.

For Each Question

Listen to the reader. Discuss and agree on an estimate. Ask one student to use a calculator to find the quotient. That student rounds the quotient to the nearest hundredth, and then reads the quotient. Every player who has the digit in the hundredths place in the quotient can remove one cube that shows the answer.

How to Win

The first player who removes both cubes wins. Have fun!

a	Divide 2,891 by 68. The quotient has which digit in the hundredths place?
b	Divide 9,027 by 49. The quotient has which digit in the hundredths place?
c	Divide 1,378 by 39. The quotient has which digit in the hundredths place?
d	Divide 5,917 by 53. The quotient has which digit in the hundredths place?
e	Divide 4,349 by 56. The quotient has which digit in the hundredths place?
f	Divide 4,038 by 86. The quotient has which digit in the hundredths place?
g	Divide 2,770 by 48. The quotient has which digit in the hundredths place?
h	Divide 8,236 by 68. The quotient has which digit in the hundredths place?
i	Divide 3,691 by 87. The quotient has which digit in the hundredths place?
j	Divide 9,957 by 71. The quotient has which digit in the hundredths place?
k	Divide 7,268 by 97. The quotient has which digit in the hundredths place?
l	Divide 4,747 by 55. The quotient has which digit in the hundredths place?
m	Divide 1,651 by 57. The quotient has which digit in the hundredths place?

n	Divide 7,780 by 12. The quotient has which digit in the hundredths place?
o	Divide 8,195 by 34. The quotient has which digit in the hundredths place?
p	Divide 6,505 by 49. The quotient has which digit in the hundredths place?
q	Divide 8,163 by 22. The quotient has which digit in the hundredths place?
r	Divide 6,566 by 11. The quotient has which digit in the hundredths place?
s	Divide 2,059 by 60. The quotient has which digit in the hundredths place?
t	Divide 8,340 by 21. The quotient has which digit in the hundredths place?
u	Divide 9,053 by 64. The quotient has which digit in the hundredths place?
v	Divide 5,438 by 92. The quotient has which digit in the hundredths place?
w	Divide 3,802 by 43. The quotient has which digit in the hundredths place?
x	Divide 6,154 by 97. The quotient has which digit in the hundredths place?
y	Divide 2,891 by 67. The quotient has which digit in the hundredths place?
z	Divide 7,077 by 97. The quotient has which digit in the hundredths place?

Play another game. Begin with the next question in the list. Or make up your own questions like these. Play the game with your questions.

Get Started (or)

Put 1 2 3 4 in a bag.

For Each Round

Choose A, B, C, D, E, or **F**. Ask someone to read the problem.
Pick a tile. Pick two tiles if your group has only two students.
Read the sentence next to your number when it is your turn.
Discuss: Which sentences have extra information that is not needed? Which sentences have information that is needed?
Decide: What is the answer to the question?

A John bought popcorn and a drink. How much did he spend for his snack?

1	**John went to the 2:00 P.M. movie.**
2	**A drink costs $1.50.**
3	**Five tickets cost $30.00.**
4	**Popcorn costs $2.50.**

B It takes 3 cups of flour to make 1 cake. How much milk is used to make the cake?

1	**A quart of milk contains 32 ounces.**
2	**2 tablespoons of vanilla are needed for 1 cake.**
3	**The recipe for 1 cake calls for 1 cup of milk.**
4	**3 cakes are being made.**

C It takes Mary 1 hour to walk 3 miles. John walks for 45 minutes. What is the difference in the times that they walked?

1	**John and Mary each walked 3 miles.**
2	**John and Mary live 20 miles apart.**
3	**John takes 45 minutes to walk 3 miles.**
4	**John and Mary rested for 1 hour after they walked.**

D Susan drove her car from Houston to Los Angeles. How much did she pay for gasoline?

1	**Susan's car uses 1 gallon to go 30 miles.**
2	**Susan took 3 people with her.**
3	**Gasoline costs $3.00 for 1 gallon.**
4	**The distance from Houston to Los Angeles is 1,500 miles.**

E Bill bought 3 times as many bananas as Tom. How much did Bill pay for the bananas?

1	**Bananas cost 50¢ for each pound.**
2	**Tom bought 12 apples and 6 potatoes.**
3	**Tom bought 3 bananas.**
4	**3 bananas cost 60¢.**

F Ann bought 3 chairs for $20 each. She sold some to Bill. How much did Bill pay for each chair?

1	**Ann paid $30 for each of two tables.**
2	**Ann sold Tom 2 lamps for $50 each.**
3	**Ann sold Bill 2 chairs.**
4	**Ann sold each chair to Bill for $4 more than she paid for it.**

If you have more time Make up a "Think Together" question with extra and missing information. Challenge your classmates to think together to answer your question.

Put 1 2 3 4 in a bag.

For Each Round

Choose A, B, C, D, E, or F. Ask someone to read the problem.
Pick a tile. Pick two tiles if your group has only two students.
Read the sentence next to your number when it is your turn.
Discuss: Which sentences have extra information that is not needed? Which sentences have information that is needed?
Decide: What is the answer to the question?

A Mary and her friends each had 1 sandwich, 1 drink and 1 cookie. How much did all the lunches cost?

1	**1 piece of pie is $1.50.**
 2	**4 cookies cost $2.00.**
 3	**Mary had 3 friends with her.**
 4	**1 sandwich and 1 drink cost $3.00.**

B Mary had 4 more pens than Paulo. How much did Mary spend for her pens?

 1	**Paulo gave 5 pencils to Jane.**
 2	**Paulo and Mary had 10 pens in all.**
 3	**10 pencils cost $5.00.**
 4	**4 pens cost $8.00.**

C Bill served a breakfast with 2 eggs, 1 cup of fruit and 2 toasts on each plate. How many loaves of bread did he need?

 1	**Each fruit cup had 7 berries and 1 peach.**
 2	**A loaf of bread has 26 slices.**
 3	**Breakfast cost $7.00.**
 4	**Bill served breakfast to 39 people.**

D A freight train has 20 times the cars that a passenger train has. How many empty boxcars does the freight train have?

 1	**There are 4 more full boxcars than empty ones.**
 2	**The freight train has 10 coal cars.**
 3	**1/2 the cars in the freight train are boxcars.**
 4	**The passenger train has 5 sleek silver cars.**

E A decorator puts 2 curtains in each window of a building. How much did the project cost?

 1	**Each curtain costs $80.00.**
 2	**The building has 12 stories.**
 3	**Each story has 4 doors.**
 4	**Each story has 25 windows.**

F Alice can buy 4 balloons for $1.00. How many balloons did Alice buy?

 1	**Alice has 2 times as much money as Tom.**
 2	**Alice has 8 dollars to buy balloons.**
 3	**Tom bought 6 balloons for $2.00.**
 4	**Tom has 2 more dollars than Mary.**

If you have more time Make up a "Think Together" question with extra and missing information. Challenge your classmates to think together to answer your question.

Get Started Get 10 squares in one color and 10 in another color, two paper clips, and two number cubes. Take turns.

At Your Turn Toss two cubes to find your ovals. **EXAMPLE:** Choose the 3rd oval on the left and the 5th oval on the right, **or** choose the 5th oval on the left and the 3rd oval on the right. Mark your ovals with paper clips.

How to Play The numbers that you chose are factors. Explain how to multiply those factors. Say an equation that includes the product. Find and cover the product. Lose your turn if the answer is taken.

How to Win The first player or team to get any three connected rectangles in a row or column wins.

Left ovals: 0.05, 1.28, 93.21, 100.08, 0.05, 1.28

12.8	9,321	0.5	1,000.8
5	100.08	932.1	100,080
93,210	128	93.21	0.05
1.28	10,008	50	1,280

Right ovals: 10, 100, 1,000, 1, 100, 1,000

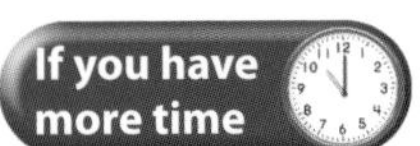

Play again! If you need to annex one or more zeros, explain why.

Center Activity **6-1**

Get Started  Get 10 squares in one color and 10 in another color, one paper clip, and one number cube. Take turns.

At Your Turn Toss one cube to find your oval. **EXAMPLE:** Choose the 3rd oval on the left, **or** choose the 3rd oval on the right. Mark your oval with a paper clip.

How to Play The number you chose is a product. Find the expression that you can compute to get that product. Explain how patterns help you find the product. Cover the answer. Lose your turn if the answer is taken.

How to Win The first player or team to get any three connected rectangles in a row or column wins.

Left ovals					Right ovals
8					1,800
50	81.2 x 10	73.2 x 100	0.4 x 1,000	0.0007 x 100	9,300
0.07	0.8 x 10	20.02 x 10	10.6 x 10	4.5 x 100	7,320
450	1.8 x 1,000	9.3 x 1,000	0.0007 x 100	10.6 x 10	400
200.2	0.08 x 100	0.5 x 100	2.002 x 100	8.9 x 100	890
812					106

Play again! Talk about your strategy as you play.

Put 1 2 3 4 in a bag.

For Each Round

Choose A, B, C, or D.
Pick a tile. Pick two tiles if your group has only two students.
Read the expression next to your number when it is your turn.
Explain the method you use to estimate the product.
Decide: Does the estimate make sense? Why?

A

Estimate each product using rounding. Which estimates are less than 100?

	**0.12 × 6**
	**0.904 × 77**
	**0.698 × 5**
	**214.2 × 9**

B

Estimate each product using compatible numbers. Which of the estimates is a three-digit number?

	**38.2 × 26**
	**199.1 × 24**
	**2.18 × 16**
	**9.25 × 21**

C

Estimate each product using rounding. Then, estimate using compatible numbers. Compare your estimates.

	**4.1 × 24**
	**3.02 × 16**
	**78.9 × 94**
	**3.98 × 17**

D

Use any method to estimate the product. Say which method you choose. Explain the steps you use to make an estimate.

	**0.79 × 52**
	**3.04 × 11**
	**33.08 × 200**
	**25 × 0.38**

Make up two factors like these.
Challenge your group members to estimate the product.

Put 1 2 3 4 in a bag.

For Each Round

Choose A, B, C, or D.
Pick a tile. Pick two tiles if your group has only two students.
Read the expression next to your number when it is your turn.
Explain how to estimate the product.
Decide: Does the estimate make sense? Why?

A Use compatible numbers to estimate each product.	
1	**39.5 × 26**
2	**19.4 × 24**
3	**2.13 × 16**
4	**19.6 × 24**

B Estimate by rounding each number to the greatest place that has a non-zero digit.	
1	**3.25 × 18**
2	**2.14 × 31**
3	**1.89 × 82**
4	**0.91 × 125**

C Estimate the product. Then, find the exact product. Compare those two results.	
1	**0.54 × 412**
2	**9.02 × 81**
3	**33.05 × 204**
4	**3.05 × 12**

D Use the table to the right to answer these questions.	
1	**Jimmy has $10 in his wallet. About how many comic books can he buy?**
2	**Wally has $20 in his wallet. About how many DVDs can he buy?**
3	**About how many times the cost of a comic book is the cost of a DVD?**
4	**Hakeem wants 2 DVDs and a comic book. About how much will those items cost?**

Item	Cost
Comic Book	$4.90
DVD	$9.50

Make up a question about the data in the table so that your group members can practice estimating a product.

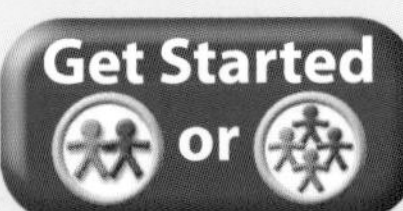
Get Started Put 1 2 3 4 in a bag.

For Each Round

Choose A, B, C, or D. Ask someone to read the directions to the group.
Pick a tile. Pick two tiles if your group has only two students.
Read the phrase or expression next to your tile number when it is your turn.
Discuss your phrase or expression.
Explain your answer. Ask your group members to tell you why your answer is or is not correct.

A

State an algebraic expression for each word phrase. Let n stand for the number.

1	**Five less than a number times 3**
2	**Sixty minus three times a number**
3	**Two more than six times a number**
4	**Ten less than nine times a number**

B

Which of the following word phrases can be written as $7n + 2$?

1	**Two times a number, plus 7**
2	**Two more than seven times a number**
3	**Seven more than a number**
4	**Seven times a number, plus 2**

C

Use mental math to evaluate each expression for $n = 5$.

1	$8n + 6$
2	$7n - 2$
3	$10n + 10$
4	$5n - 5$

D

State an algebraic expression for each word phrase. Let x stand for the number.

1	**Eight plus a number times 5**
2	**Nine plus a number times 6**
3	**Thirty minus three times a number**
4	**Seventy minus six times a number**

If you have more time Make up an algebraic expression. Ask your group members to say a word phrase that corresponds to your algebraic expression.

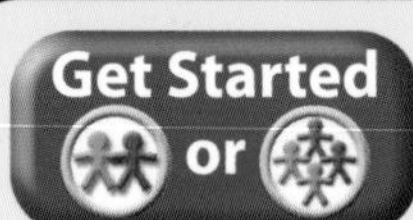

Put 1 2 3 4 in a bag.

For Each Round

Choose A, B, C, or D. Ask someone to read the directions to the group.
Pick a tile. Pick two tiles if your group has only two students.
Read the phrase or expression next to your tile number when it is your turn.
Discuss your phrase or expression.
Explain your answer. Ask your group members to tell you why your answer is or is not correct.

A

Say an algebraic expression for each word phrase. Let *n* stand for the number.

1	**Fifteen plus three times a number**
2	**Nine minus half of a number**
3	**Six minus two times a number**
4	**One plus eight times a number**

B

Say a word phrase for each algebraic expression.

1	$5x + 9$
2	$2x - 1$
3	$100x + 6$
4	$30x - 10$

C

Say an algebraic expression for each word phrase. Let *n* stand for the number. Then, say another word phrase which has the same meaning.

1	**Ten less than nine times a number**
2	**Two more than six times a number**
3	**Five less than a number times 3**
4	**Sixty minus three times a number**

D

Use mental math to evaluate each expression for $x = 0$.

1	$2x + 2$
2	$2 - 2x$
3	$9 - 3x$
4	$8x + 9$

If you have more time Say a word phrase that corresponds to an algebraic expression. Ask your group members to state an algebraic expression for your word phrase.

Tic Tac Toe

Get Started  Get 20 squares in one color and 20 in another color. Get paper and a pencil. Get two number cubes for players to share. Take turns.

For Each Round Toss two cubes. Form a decimal by writing the two numbers with a decimal point between them. Form a second decimal by reversing the digits on either side of the decimal point. Explain how to multiply those decimals. If you toss a double, for example, 3 and 3, multiply 3.3×3.3. Cover the product. If the answer is taken, lose your turn.

Example The decimals are **3.5** and **5.3**. Explain how to multiply **3.5 × 5.3**.

How to Win The first player or team to cover a row, column, or diagonal in one of the four sections of the game board wins.

18.55	5.74	2.52	29.44	9.76	36.4
30.25	1.21	10.08	24.3	19.36	14.62
4.03	13	7.36	16.12	7.65	22.68
22.68	14.62	36.4	5.74	13	7.36
7.65	10.89	9.76	18.55	43.56	4.84
29.44	16.12	24.3	4.03	10.08	2.52

If you have more time Play again!

Tic Tac Toe

Get Started  Get 20 squares in one color and 20 in another color. Get paper and a pencil. Get two number cubes for players to share. Take turns.

For Each Round Toss two cubes. Order the numbers you get from least to greatest. Form a decimal by placing a decimal point between the two numbers. Form a second decimal by placing the decimal point to the left of both numbers. Explain how to multiply those two decimals. If you toss a double, for example 3 and 3, multiply 3.3 × 0.33. Cover the product. If the answer is taken, lose your turn.

Example The decimals are **3.5** and **0.35.** Explain how to multiply **3.5 × 0.35.**

How to Win The first player or team to cover a row, column, or diagonal in one of the four sections of the game board wins.

1.024	0.676	3.136	0.441	4.225	2.809
3.969	1.936	0.576	1.681	1.089	0.529
0.256	1.156	0.169	3.844	2.601	2.025
0.961	2.916	3.721	0.484	0.196	0.144
4.096	0.121	0.225	1.225	4.356	0.625
1.849	1.764	3.025	2.116	2.704	1.296

Play again!

Get 10 squares in one color and 10 in another color.
Get two number cubes. Take turns with another player or team.
Talk about math as you play!

At Your Turn

Toss two number cubes. Add the dots. Find your toss below.
Follow the directions. Explain your thinking. Cover the answer.
If the answer is taken, lose your turn. Have fun!

Toss	Get paper and a pencil. Say the factors. Explain how to estimate the product. Find the product.
2	9.8 x 2
3	56 x 0.4
4	0.1 x 388
5	63.2 x 20
6	57 x 2.2
7	350 x 2.75
8	405 x 0.9
9	29 x 4.1
10	84 x 0.05
11	0.1 x 29
12	0.67 x 8

125.4	364.5	962.5	22.4
5.36	118.9	1,264	364.5
1,264	4.2	19.6	118.9
2.9	962.5	125.4	38.8

How to Win

You win if you are the first to get four connected rectangles, like:

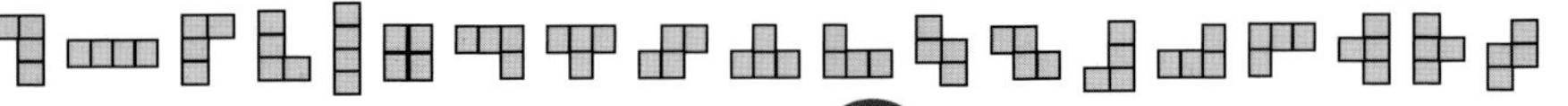

Play again!

Get Started

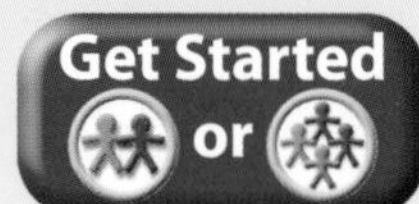

Get 10 squares in one color and 10 in another color.
Get two number cubes. Get paper and a pencil. Take turns with another player or team. Talk about math as you play!

At Your Turn

Toss two number cubes. Add the dots. Find your toss below.
Follow the directions. Explain your thinking. Cover the answer.
If the answer is taken, lose your turn. Have fun!

Toss	This number is a product. Find two factors you can multiply to get this product. Use estimation to help you. Explain your choice.
2	9.7
3	6.54
4	0.025
5	44.1
6	149.12
7	1,085.85
8	69.6
9	205.6
10	311.4
11	36.09
12	9.6

0.8 x 12	5.8 x 12	2.1 x 21	0.01 x 654
16 x 9.32	0.1 x 97	285 x 3.81	514 x 0.4
2.1 x 21	285 x 3.81	514 x 0.4	0.001 x 25
4.01 x 9	16 x 9.32	5.8 x 12	34.6 x 9

How to Win

You win if you are the first to get four connected rectangles, like:

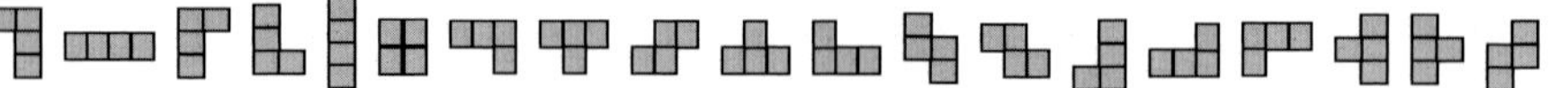

Play again!

Display the Digits

0 1 2 3 4 5 6 7 8 9

Get paper and a pencil.
Explain how to multiply the two decimals.
Display each 0 – 9 tile exactly once.
If you have a partner, take turns.

3.8 x 2.4 = [a] . [b] 2

32.3 x 0.8 = 2 [c] .84

$$\begin{array}{r} 11.1 \\ \times\ 6.1 \\ \hline \end{array}$$

[d] [e] .71

$$\begin{array}{r} 37.2 \\ \times\ 3.4 \\ \hline \end{array}$$

126 [f] [g]

0.41 x 0.3 = [h] .1 [i] [j]

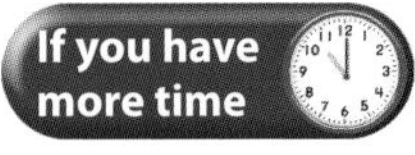

Make up other puzzles about multiplying two decimals.
Ask your partner to display the answers with 0 – 9 tiles.

Display the Digits

0 1 2 3 4 5 6 7 8 9

Get paper and a pencil. Explain how to find each missing digit. Display each 0 – 9 tile exactly once. If you have a partner, take turns.

82.5 × [a].1 = 8.2[b]

22.1 × 0.3 = 6.[c][d]

```
   69.5[e]
×      2.1
----------
 145.9[f]2
```

```
   41.6
  × 3.4
-------
14[g].4[h]
```

6 × 0.13 = 0.[i][j]

Make up other puzzles about multiplying two decimals. Ask your partner to display the answers with 0 – 9 tiles.

Teamwork

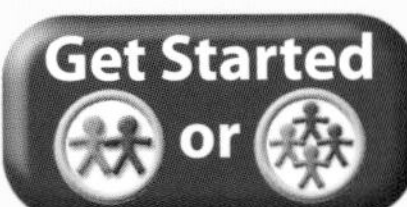

Get paper and a pencil.
Put 1 2 3 4 in a bag.

Repeat for Each Round

Choose **a, b,** or **c**. Ask someone to read the problem aloud.
Pick a tile. Pick two tiles if your group has only two students.
Follow the directions next to your number when it is your turn.

Do These Steps In Order

Ask questions about the problem so that your group can determine which operations you would use to solve the problem.

Ask a question so that your group can determine which operation to use first.

Ask a question so that your group can determine which operation to use second.

Ask a question so that your group can solve the problem. Work together to solve it. Decide if you could have changed the order in which you used the operations.

a. In his bank, Tom has 8 quarters, 12 dimes, 9 nickels, and 13 pennies. How much money does he have in all?

b. Hank spends $75 at the fair. He spends $12 on food and $39 on souvenirs. He spends the rest on rides. How much does he spend on rides?

c. Tasha took 19 photos at her family reunion and 85 photos on her vacation. She wants to put the pictures in an album that will hold 8 photos on each page. How many pages does she need for her photographs?

Make up another problem that can be solved by using more than one operation. Ask a partner to solve your problem.

Teamwork

Get paper and a pencil.
Put  in a bag.

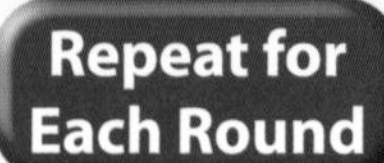

Choose **a, b,** or **c**. Ask someone to read the problem aloud.
Pick a tile. Pick two tiles if your group has only two students.
Follow the directions next to your number when it is your turn.

Do These Steps in Order

 **Ask questions about the problem so that your group can determine which operations you would use to solve the problem.**

 **Ask a question so that your group can determine which operation to use first.**

 **Ask a question so that your group can determine which operation to use second.**

 **Ask a question so that your group can solve the problem. Work together to solve it. Decide if you could have changed the order in which you used the operations.**

a. Serena practices her violin for three hours every day and takes singing lessons twice a week for two hours each time. How many hours does Serena spend on her music each week?

b. Martina sells small, medium, and large snack bars. She sells the bars for 25 cents, 50 cents and $1.00. She sells 12 large bars and 15 small bars. How much does she collect altogether?

c. Eric wants to buy some baseball cards that cost 35 cents each. He has 5 quarters, 7 dimes, 8 nickels, and 15 pennies. How many cards can he buy?

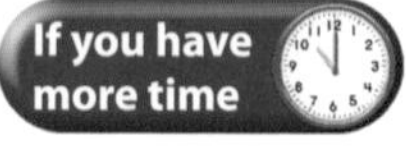

Make up another problem that can be solved by using more than one operation. Ask a partner to solve your problem.

Get Started Get 10 squares in one color and 10 in another color, two paper clips, and two number cubes. Take turns.

At Your Turn Toss two cubes to find your ovals. **EXAMPLE:** Choose the 3rd oval on the left and the 5th oval on the right, **or** choose the 5th oval on the left and the 3rd oval on the right. Mark your ovals with paper clips.

How to Play Explain how to divide the number you chose on the left by the number you chose on the right. Say an equation that includes the quotient. Find and cover the quotient. Lose your turn if the answer is taken.

How to Win The first player or team to get any three connected rectangles in a row or column wins.

Left ovals: 138.2, 205.6, 9,763, 2.6, 138.2, 205.6

976.3	13.82	0.26	2.056
138.2	20.56	97.63	1.382
0.0026	9,763	205.6	0.026
0.2056	2.6	0.1382	9.763

Right ovals: 10, 100, 1,000, 1, 100, 1,000

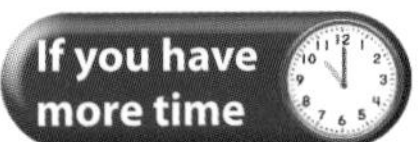

Play again! Talk about patterns that help you to divide.

Center Activity **7-1** ★★

Clip and Cover

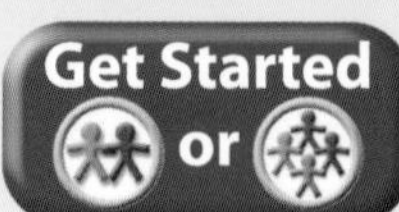

Get Started or: Get 10 squares in one color and 10 in another color, one paper clip, and one number cube. Take turns.

At Your Turn: Toss one cube to find your oval. **EXAMPLE:** Choose the 3rd oval on the left, **or** choose the 3rd oval on the right. Mark your oval with a paper clip.

How to Play: The number you chose is a quotient. Find the expression that you can compute to get that quotient. Explain how patterns help you to find the quotient. Cover the answer. Lose your turn if the answer is taken.

How to Win: The first player or team to get any three connected rectangles in a row or column wins.

Left ovals: 0.602, 1.06, 0.08, 8.12, 0.732, 0.934

81.2 ÷ 10	73.2 ÷ 100	0.4 ÷ 1,000	93.6 ÷ 100
0.8 ÷ 10	20.02 ÷ 10	10.6 ÷ 10	94.5 ÷ 10
934 ÷ 1,000	6.02 ÷ 10	200.2 ÷ 100	786.2 ÷ 10
945 ÷ 100	936 ÷ 1,000	5 ÷ 100	812 ÷ 100

Right ovals: 0.05, 2.002, 9.45, 78.62, 0.936, 0.0004

Play again! Talk about your strategy as you play.

Put 1 2 3 4 in a bag.

For Each Round

Choose A, B, C, or D. Ask someone to read the directions.
Pick a tile. Pick two tiles if your group has only two students.
Read the division expression next to your tile number.
Ask your group to estimate the quotient when it is your turn.
Decide if each group member's estimate is reasonable for your division expression.

A Estimate each quotient using rounding.

1	**34.25 ÷ 6**
2	**81.3 ÷ 2**
3	**200.06 ÷ 5**
4	**71.9 ÷ 10**

B Estimate each quotient using compatible numbers.

1	**19.45 ÷ 4**
2	**23.6 ÷ 5**
3	**62.6 ÷ 8**
4	**124.5 ÷ 65**

C Estimate each quotient using rounding. Then, estimate using compatible numbers. Compare your estimates.

1	**105.6 ÷ 11**
2	**48.8 ÷ 7**
3	**128.6 ÷ 65**
4	**31.77 ÷ 7**

D Use any method to estimate the quotient. Tell which method you used.

1	**195.6 ÷ 12**
2	**270.9 ÷ 90**
3	**88.34 ÷ 2**
4	**13.5 ÷ 7**

Make up a division expression.
Challenge your classmates to think together to estimate the quotient.

Get Started ... or ...

Put 1 2 3 4 in a bag.
Get paper and a pencil.

For Each Round

Choose A, B, C, or D. Ask someone to read the directions.
Pick a tile. Pick two tiles if your group has only two students.
Read the information next to your tile number.
Explain how to follow the directions when it is your turn.
Ask group members if they agree with your answer.

A	Use compatible numbers to estimate each quotient.
1	31.2 ÷ 7.9
2	124.9 ÷ 65
3	23.4 ÷ 6
4	62.6 ÷ 8

B	Create a division expression that would have the given estimated quotient.
1	40
2	5
3	100
4	35

C	Estimate the quotient. Then, find the exact quotient. Compare it with your estimate.
1	20.47 ÷ 23
2	154.4 ÷ 8
3	153.92 ÷ 32
4	427.5 ÷ 6

D	Sally has $35.50 and Betty has $41.20. At the book store, magazines cost $3. Paperbacks cost $6. Use this information to answer each question.
1	About how many magazines can Sally purchase?
2	About how many paperbacks can Sally purchase?
3	About how many magazines can Betty purchase?
4	About how many paperbacks can Betty purchase?

Make up a division expression.
Challenge your classmates to think together to estimate the quotient.

Get 10 squares in one color and 10 in another color.
Get two number cubes. Take turns with another player or team.
Talk about math as you play!

At Your Turn

Toss two number cubes. Add the dots. Find your toss below.
Follow the directions. Cover the answer. If the answer is taken, lose your turn. Have fun!

Toss	Get paper and a pencil. Read the expression. Explain how to find the quotient.
2	4.69 ÷ 7
3	13.932 ÷ 9
4	3.534 ÷ 6
5	162.0 ÷ 4
6	153.92 ÷ 32
7	49.92 ÷ 16
8	945.25 ÷ 19
9	427.5 ÷ 6
10	2.035 ÷ 5
11	615.34 ÷ 10
12	40.24 ÷ 8

0.407	3.12	40.5	0.67
49.75	5.03	4.81	61.534
4.81	49.75	0.589	40.5
1.548	71.25	3.12	71.25

How to Win

You win if you are the first to get four connected rectangles, like:

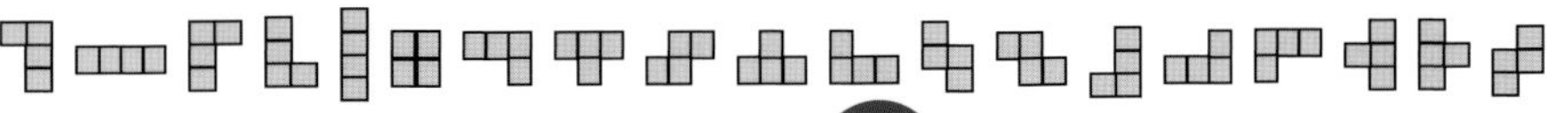

Play again!

Center Activity **7-3** ★★

Get Started 

Get 10 squares in one color and 10 in another color.
Get two number cubes. Take turns with another player or team.
Talk about math as you play!

At Your Turn

Toss two number cubes. Add the dots. Find your toss below.
Follow the directions. Explain your thinking. Cover the answer.
If the answer is taken, lose your turn. Have fun!

Toss	Get paper and a pencil. This number is the missing digit in a quotient. Find a quotient that has this missing digit.
2	1
3	3
4	4
5	8
6	5
7	9
8	7
9	0
10	2
11	1
12	6

4.5 ÷ 10 = 0.☐5	56.8 ÷ 2 = 2☐.4	6.16 ÷ 88 = 0.0☐	20.47 ÷ 23 = ☐.89
113.6 ÷ 8 = 14.☐	27.5 ÷ 25 = 1.☐	25.5 ÷ 25 = 1.☐2	8.1 ÷ 9 = 0.☐
22.5 ÷ 15 = 1.☐	12.25 ÷ 35 = 0.3☐	53.2 ÷ 28 = 1.☐	36.6 ÷ 60 = 0.☐1
20.5 ÷ 5 = 4.☐	55.5 ÷ 15 = 3.☐	212.5 ÷ 25 = ☐.5	2.4 ÷ 8 = 0.☐

How to Win

You win if you are the first to get four connected rectangles, like:

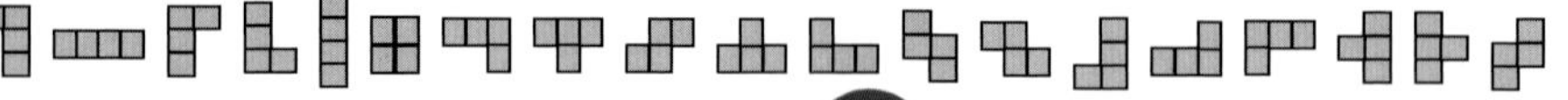

Play again!

Clip and Cover

Get Started (or) Get 10 squares in one color and 10 in another color, one paper clip, paper and a pencil, and one number cube. Take turns.

At Your Turn Toss one cube to find your oval. **EXAMPLE:** Choose the 3rd oval on the left, **or** choose the 3rd oval on the right. Mark your oval with a paper clip.

How to Play Say the dividend and the divisor in the oval you chose. Explain how to estimate the quotient. Then multiply the dividend and the divisor by the power of ten that makes the divisor a whole number. Find the quotient. Cover the answer. Lose your turn if the answer is taken.

How to Win The first player or team to get any three connected rectangles in a row or column wins.

Left ovals:
1. 1,508 ÷ 0.52
2. 37,740 ÷ 7.4
3. 0.39)1,989
4. 3,721 ÷ 0.61
5. 0.19)1,539
6. 4.9)4,753

51,000	200	79,000	5,100
5,600	58,000	6,100	1,700
2,900	1,500	5,100	6,100
200	79,000	8,100	970

Right ovals:
1. 122 ÷ 0.61
2. 0.08)6,320
3. 12,180 ÷ 0.21
4. 1.23)6,888
5. 405 ÷ 0.27
6. 5.61)9,537

If you have more time Play again! Talk about how estimating can help you identify quotients on the game board that are or that are not reasonable.

Get Started (or) Get 10 squares in one color and 10 in another color, two paper clips, and two number cubes. Take turns.

At Your Turn Toss two cubes to find your ovals. **EXAMPLE:** [3] [5] Choose the 3rd oval on the left and the 5th oval on the right, **or** choose the 5th oval on the left and the 3rd oval on the right. Mark your ovals with paper clips.

How to Play Estimate the quotient of the number in the left oval divided by the number in the right oval. Then multiply the dividend and the divisor by the power of 10 that makes the divisor a whole number. Find the quotient. Cover the answer. Lose your turn if the answer is taken.

How to Win The first player or team to get any three connected rectangles in a row or column wins.

Left ovals: 360, 252, 288, 504, 360, 252

210	14,400	25,200	4,200
12,600	120	2,400	1,400
18,000	2,100	105	2,800
3,000	2,000	1,600	150

Right ovals: 0.02, 0.12, 0.18, 2.4, 0.12, 0.18

Play again! Talk about your strategies as you play.

Teamwork

Get Started 

Get paper and a pencil.
Put 1 2 3 4 in a bag.

Repeat for Each Round

Choose **a**, **b**, **c**, **d**, **e**, or **f**.
Pick a tile. Pick two tiles if your group has only two students.
Do the jobs listed below in order.
To find your job, find the number that matches the tile you chose.

 **Use compatible numbers to estimate the quotient.**

 **Multiply the divisor and dividend by a power of ten that makes the divisor a whole number. Explain.**

 **Divide the new dividend by the new divisor to find the quotient.**

 **Check to see if your quotient is close to your estimate.**

☆☆☆ Divide by a Decimal ☆☆☆

a.	6.3 ÷ 0.9	**b.**	36.6 ÷ 0.6
c.	5.25 ÷ 2.5	**d.**	4.84 ÷ 2.2
e.	0.82 ÷ 41.2	**f.**	1.64 ÷ 0.04

If you have $9.00 in quarters, how many quarters do you have? Use steps 1 – 4 to find out.

Teamwork

Get paper and a pencil.
Put 1 2 3 4 in a bag.

Repeat for Each Round

Choose **a, b, c, d, e,** or **f.**
Pick a tile. Pick two tiles if your group has only two students.
Do the jobs listed below in order.
To find your job, find the number that matches the tile you chose.

 **Use compatible numbers to estimate the quotient.**

 **Multiply the divisor and dividend by the same number that makes the divisor a whole number. Explain.**

 **Divide the new dividend by the new divisor to find the quotient.**

 **Check to see if your quotient is close to your estimate.**

☆☆☆ Divide by a Decimal ☆☆☆

a.	$0.19 \div 0.55$	**b.**	$1.89 \div 0.09$
c.	$7.35 \div 0.07$	**d.**	$0.96 \div 0.24$
e.	$6.41 \div 1.23$	**f.**	$4.27 \div 1.22$

If you have $17.00 in nickels, how many nickels do you have? Use steps 1 – 4 to find out.

Display the Digits

0 1 2 3 4 5 6 7 8 9

Read a problem. Ask the hidden question or questions. Explain how to solve the problem. Use tiles to show the missing digits. Display each 0 – 9 tile exactly once. If you have a partner, take turns.

Travis went to the supermarket to buy some food for his mother. He bought 1.5 pounds of cheese at $4.24 a pound. He bought 2.5 pounds of sandwich meats at $3.62 a pound. How much did Travis spend?

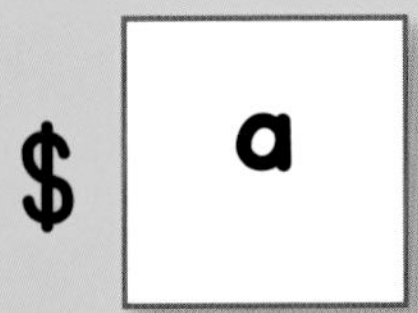

$ [a] . [b] 5  $ [c] . [d] 6 

Total = $1 [e] . [f] 1

Wendy is baking cakes for a bake sale. The store sells a dozen eggs for $1.56. Wendy decides to find the price of one egg. Then, she will use that to determine how much she will spend on the 6 eggs she will use in her recipes.

$1.56 ÷ 1 [g] = $0. [h] 3 per egg

$0. [i] [j] cost of 6 eggs

a	b	c	d	e
f	g	h	i	j

Make up another puzzle with a multiple-step problem. Ask your partner to display the answers with 0 – 9 tiles.

Read a problem. Ask the hidden question or questions. Explain how to solve the problem. Use tiles to show the missing digits. Display each 0 – 9 tile exactly once. If you have a partner, take turns.

Tran earned $7.26 an hour for working 22.5 hours last week. After getting a raise, Tran earned $7.76 an hour this week. If Tran worked 23.5 hours this week, how much did Tran earn in all for both weeks?

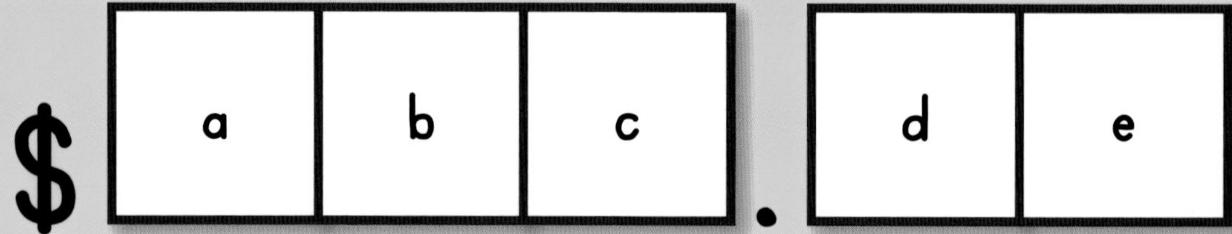

Felicia purchases two identical jackets, one for her and one for a friend. She has a $10 coupon. What is the original cost of one jacket if her total bill (after the coupon was subtracted) is $129.60?

Billy and Susie were playing a numbers game. Billy gave Susie a number. Billy then told Susie to multiply that number by 6.9. Next, Billy told Susie to divide the new number by 3. Susie got 4.6. What number did Billy originally give Susie?

Make up another digit puzzle with one or more multiple-step problems. Ask your partner to display the answers with 0 – 9 tiles.

Get Started — Get 10 squares in one color and 10 in another color, two paper clips, and two number cubes. Take turns.

At Your Turn — Toss two cubes to find your ovals. **EXAMPLE:** Choose the 3rd oval on the left and the 5th oval on the right, **or** choose the 5th oval on the left and the 3rd oval on the right. Mark your ovals with paper clips.

How to Play — Read the word phrase in your left oval followed by the word phrase in your right oval. Find the corresponding algebraic expression. Explain your choice. Cover the answer. Lose your turn if the answer is taken.

How to Win — The first player or team to get any three connected rectangles in a row or column wins.

Left ovals:
1. 10 less than
2. 10 more than
3. 8 fewer than
4. 10 times
5. 10 added to
6. 8 less than

$4s - 10$	$8c - 10$	$n \div 15 - 8$	$10 \times 4s$
$10 \times \frac{100}{k}$	$100 \div k - 10$	$4s - 8$	$\frac{100}{k} - 8$
$10 \times \frac{n}{15}$	$8c - 8$	$100 \div k + 10$	$8c + 10$
$\frac{n}{15} - 10$	$4s + 10$	$n \div 15 + 10$	$10 \times 8c$

Right ovals:
1. 4 times a number s
2. a number n divided by 15
3. 8 times a number c
4. 100 divided by a number k
5. a number c times 8
6. a number n divided by 15

Play again! Does what you read first always appear first in the algebraic expression? Why not?

Get 10 squares in one color and 10 in another color, one paper clip, and one number cube. Take turns.

At Your Turn Toss one cube to find your oval. **EXAMPLE:** Choose the 3rd oval on the left, **or** choose the 3rd oval on the right. Mark your oval with a paper clip.

How to Play The variable in the algebraic expression you chose represents a number. Say a word phrase for your algebraic expression. Cover that word phrase. Lose your turn if the answer is taken.

How to Win The first player or team to get any three connected rectangles in a row or column wins.

Left ovals					Right ovals
$3s - 15$	15 less than 3 times a number	1 less than a number divided by 5	a number increased by 20	2 less than 13 times a number	$x + 20$
$17x$	8 decreased by a number	6 less than a number	25 more than 4 times a number	2 more than 7 times a number	$4x + 25$
$r \div 5$	1 more than 7 divided by a number	2 more than 7 times a number	17 times a number	15 less than 3 times a number	$\frac{b}{5} - 1$
$7k + 2$	a number divided by 5	25 more than 4 times a number	13 times a number decreased by 2	52 times a number	$8 - g$
$n - 6$					$13x - 2$
$7 \div m + 1$					$52x$

Play again! Talk about your strategies as you play.

Teamwork

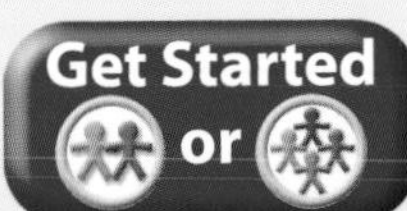

Get paper and a pencil.
Put 1 2 3 4 5 6 7 8 9 in a bag.

Repeat for Each Round

Choose **A**, **B**, **C**, or **D**. Take turns.
On your turn, pick tiles from the bag until you fill each blank space.
Explain how to use the order of operations.
Tell your team the value of the expression. Put the tiles back in the bag.
After every team member has taken a turn, begin a new round.

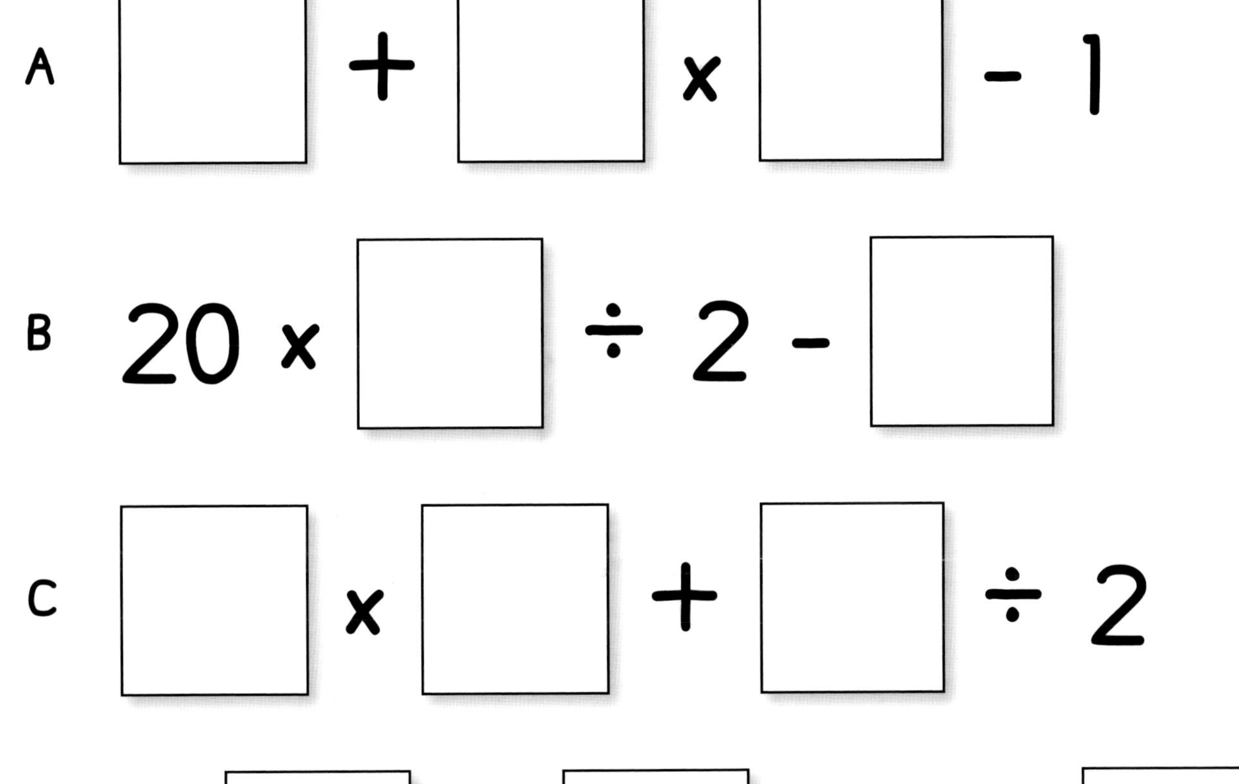

Play again! This time, use mental math. Or make up an order of operations puzzle like one of these. Ask your partner to pick tiles and solve your puzzle.

Teamwork

Put 1 2 3 4 5 6 7 8 9 in a bag.

Repeat for Each Round

Pick two tiles. Place them in the empty spaces to show values for x and y. Take turns. On your turn, use mental math and the order of operations. Explain how to evaluate an expression for the chosen values of x and y. After every expression is evaluated, put the tiles back in the bag. Begin the next round.

$x = \square \qquad y = \square$

a	$20x - 2y$	b	$6(x + y) \div 2$
c	$3y + x \div 2 - x$	d	$40y - 3x$
e	$y(5 + x)$	f	$30y - (x + 7)$
g	$50y - x + 7$	h	$100 - 2(x + y)$

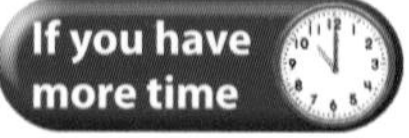

Try $x(100 + y) - 75$ or $y(100 - x) + 75$.

Get Started Put 1 2 3 4 in a bag. Get paper and a pencil.

For Each Round

Choose A, B, C, D, E, or F. Ask someone to read the directions.
Pick a tile. Pick two tiles if your group has only two students.
Evaluate the expression for the value of the variable next to your tile number.
Ask your team members if they agree with your answer.

A	Find the value of the expression: $9 + 14 \div 2 - x$
1	$x = 5$
2	$x = 2$
3	$x = 9$
4	$x = 4$

B	Find the value of the expression: $k - 2 \times (8 - 6)$
1	$k = 10$
2	$k = 15$
3	$k = 20$
4	$k = 25$

C	Find the value of the expression: $33 - 4 \times w$
1	$w = 6$
2	$w = 5$
3	$w = 2$
4	$w = 4$

D	Find the value of the expression: $18 + 5 \times 3 - y$
1	$y = 9$
2	$y = 12$
3	$y = 16$
4	$y = 24$

E	Find the value of the expression: $3 \times 19 - (k + 9)$
1	$k = 17$
2	$k = 19$
3	$k = 21$
4	$k = 24$

F	Find the value of the expression: $24 \div b + (20 - 8)$
1	$b = 2$
2	$b = 4$
3	$b = 6$
4	$b = 8$

Make up an expression with one variable. Challenge your team members to evaluate your expression for four different values of the variable.

Center Activity 8-3

Put 1 2 3 4 in a bag.
Get paper and a pencil.

For Each Round

Choose A, B, C, D, E, or **F**. Ask someone to read the question.
Pick a tile. Pick two tiles if your group has only two students.
Explain how to find the value of the variable for the value of the expression you are given.
Ask your team members to check your answer.

A If the expression $14 + 6 \times 8 \div y$ has the given value, what is the value of y?

1. **The value of the expression is 38.**
2. **The value of the expression is 18.**
3. **The value of the expression is 20.**
4. **The value of the expression is 22.**

B If the expression $24 \times (11 - y + 4)$ has the given value, what is the value of y?

1. **The value of the expression is 0.**
2. **The value of the expression is 120.**
3. **The value of the expression is 72.**
4. **The value of the expression is 24.**

C If the expression $42 \div y + 2 \times 6$ has the given value, what is the value of y?

1. **The value of the expression is 33.**
2. **The value of the expression is 19.**
3. **The value of the expression is 26.**
4. **The value of the expression is 14.**

D If the expression $(5 \times 6) \times (2 \times y) - 4$ has the given value, what is the value of y?

1. **The value of the expression is 56.**
2. **The value of the expression is 176.**
3. **The value of the expression is 236.**
4. **The value of the expression is 116.**

E If the expression $8 \times 9 - (w + 5)$ has the given value, what is the value of w?

1. **The value of the expression is 63.**
2. **The value of the expression is 58.**
3. **The value of the expression is 65.**
4. **The value of the expression is 62.**

F If the expression $24 \div (2 \times 6 - h) + 5$ has the given value, what is the value of h?

1. **The value of the expression is 11.**
2. **The value of the expression is 8.**
3. **The value of the expression is 9.**
4. **The value of the expression is 13.**

If you have more time Make up a "Think Together" question like one of these.
Challenge your team members to think together to answer your question.

Get Started or

Get 10 squares in one color and 10 in another color.
Get two number cubes. Take turns with another player or team.
Talk about math as you play!

At Your Turn

Toss two number cubes. Add the dots. Find your toss below.
Follow the directions. Explain your thinking. Cover the answer.
If the answer is taken, lose your turn. Have fun!

Toss	Explain how to use the correct order of operations to evaluate the expression. You may use paper and a pencil.
2	[(8 x 2.5) ÷ 4] + 1.3
3	16.4 - [44.4 ÷ 11.1] × 3
4	9.3 + [(15 - 7) × 4.5]
5	[2 × (75 ÷ 3)] - 9.7
6	5.2 + (3.6 - 2.1)
7	(6.2 + 4.3) ÷ 5
8	(8.3 - 1.7) ÷ 6
9	7.6 - (9.6 ÷ 3) × 2
10	5.3 × [(4 × 3.5) ÷ 7]
11	[(3 + 4.6) - 5.1] + 2.6
12	2.9 + (8.1 ÷ 0.9) × 3

1.2	6.3	1.1	5.1
45.3	2.1	40.3	6.7
6.7	4.4	10.6	1.2
40.3	1.1	2.1	29.9

How to Win

You win if you are the first to get four connected rectangles, like:

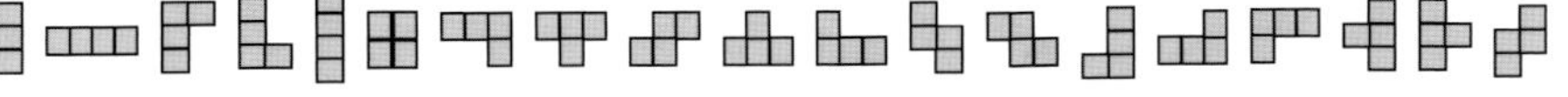

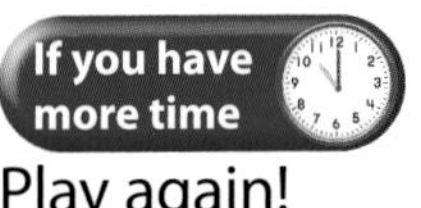

If you have more time

Play again!

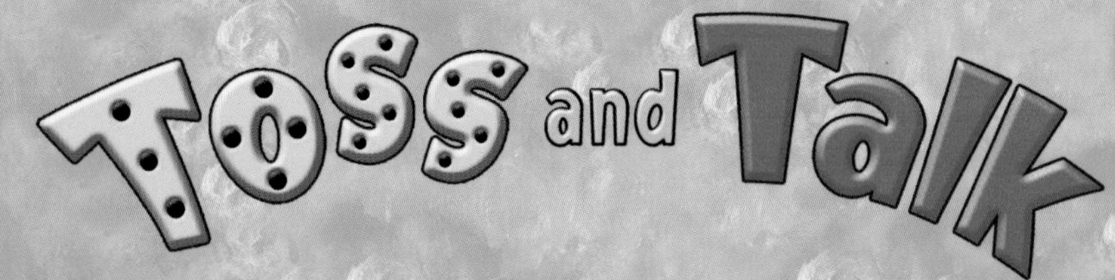

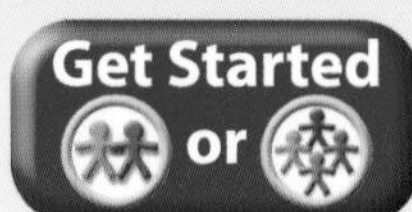

Get Started Get 10 squares in one color and 10 in another color.
Get two number cubes. Take turns with another player or team.
Talk about math as you play!

At Your Turn Toss two number cubes. Add the dots. Find your toss below.
Follow the directions. Explain your thinking. Cover the answer.
If the answer is taken, lose your turn. Have fun!

Toss	Explain how to use the correct order of operations to evaluate the expression. You may use paper and a pencil.
2	18.4 - 3.1 × 5 + 2
3	7.2 ÷ 9 + 3 - 1.6
4	4.5 ÷ 9 + 3 × 2.3
5	5 - 3.6 ÷ 6 + 1
6	9.2 - 6.3 ÷ 7
7	3.6 + 5.7 × 2
8	14.7 ÷ 7 + 8.1
9	2.5 × 2 + 3.4 - 1.6
10	4 × 3.2 - 7.2 ÷ 8
11	8.4 ÷ 4 + 2.6 × 2
12	4.9 + 10.5 ÷ 5 + 1.2

6.8	8.2	10.2	7.4
4.9	15	5.4	8.3
8.3	7.3	2.2	6.8
5.4	10.2	15	11.9

How to Win You win if you are the first to get four connected rectangles, like:

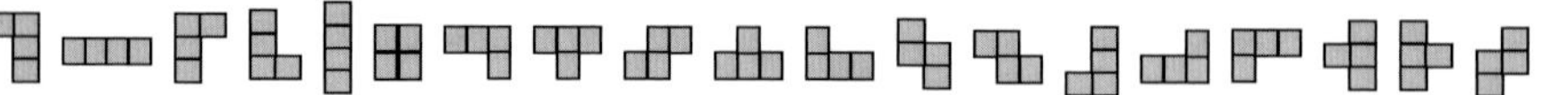

If you have more time Play again!

Display the Digits

0 1 2 3 4 5 6 7 8 9

Choose a table. Explain how each number in the bottom row is related to the one above it. Find the missing number in the expression. Display each 0 – 9 tile exactly once. If you have a partner, take turns.

n	11	13	15	17	19
n – a	7	9	11	13	15

p	1	5	9	13	17
p – f	1	5	9	13	17

p	1	3	5	7	9
p + b	8	10	12	14	16

n	1	3	5	7	9
n + g	2	4	6	8	10

n	1	2	3	4	5
n + c	6	7	8	9	10

p	5	7	8	10	11
p – h	2	4	5	7	8

p	3	4	5	6	7
p – d	1	2	3	4	5

n	1	2	3	4	5
n + i	7	8	9	10	11

n	2	4	6	8	10
n + e	11	13	15	17	19

p	8	9	10	11	12
p – j	0	1	2	3	4

a	b	c	d	e
f	g	h	i	j

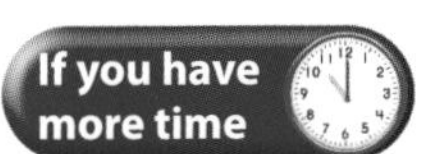

Make up other tables like these.
Ask your partner to display the missing numbers with 0 – 9 tiles.

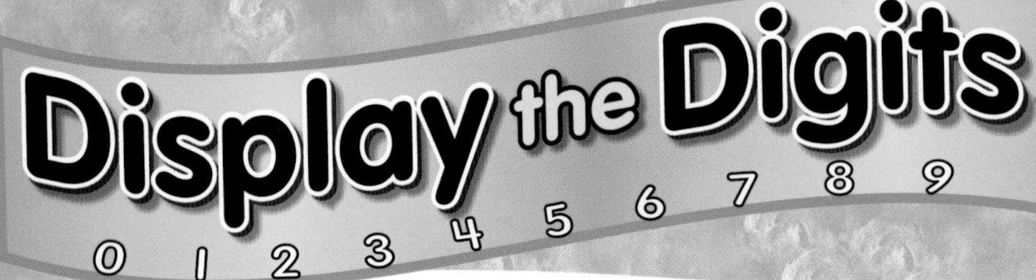

Choose a table. Look for a pattern. Find the rule. Evaluate an expression to find the missing number in the table. Use a tile to show your answer. Display each 0 – 9 tile exactly once. If you have a partner, take turns.

Dollars available	13	11	9	7	5
Dollars left after spending	9	7	5	3	a

Grade brother attends	3	2	5	1	4
Grade sister attends	6	5	8	4	b

Apples in bag	9	7	5	3	1
Apples left after sharing	8	6	4	2	c

Age of student	5	6	7	8	9
Grade attended	1	2	3	4	d

Time when work begins: ___ o'clock	1	2	3	4	5
Time when work ends: ___ o'clock	5	6	7	8	e

Grade at school	9	8	7	5	1
Next grade at school	10	9	8	6	f

Age of brother	13	12	11	10	9
Age of sister	10	9	8	7	g

Cost of item in dollars	5	7	8	10	11
Cost of item on sale	2	4	5	7	h

Eggs available	14	10	9	7	5
Eggs left after making an omelet	12	8	7	5	i

Total number of floors	8	9	10	11	12
Number of floors above the eighth floor	0	1	2	3	j

a	b
c	d
e	f
g	h
i	j

Make up other tables like these.
Ask your partner to display the missing numbers with 0 – 9 tiles.

Get 10 squares in one color and 10 in another color, two paper clips, and two number cubes. Take turns.

At Your Turn

Toss two cubes to find your ovals. **EXAMPLE:** Choose the 3rd oval on the left and the 5th table on the right, **or** choose the 5th oval on the left and the 3rd table on the right. Mark your choices with paper clips.

How to Play

Use the expression in the left column as the expression for the table you choose in the right column. Which three numbers below belong in the second row of the table? Find and cover the answer. Lose your turn if the answer is taken.

How to Win

The first player or team to get any three connected rectangles in a row or column wins.

Expressions (left ovals):

1. $n \times 3$
2. $n \div 2$
3. $n \div 4$
4. $n \times 2$
5. $n \times 3$
6. $n \div 4$

36, 12, 48	2, 3, 4	4, 6, 8	3, 1, 4
8, 10, 6	6, 2, 8	36, 24, 12	24, 8, 32
24, 36, 48	3, 2, 1	32, 40, 24	4, 5, 3
24, 16, 8	16, 24, 32	48, 60, 36	6, 4, 2

Tables (right ovals):

n	12	4	16
	□	□	□

n	12	8	4
	□	□	□

n	16	20	12
	□	□	□

n	12	4	16
	□	□	□

n	8	12	16
	□	□	□

n	12	8	4
	□	□	□

Play again! State a rule that matches each expression you choose.

Get Started  Get 10 squares in one color and 10 in another color, two paper clips, and two number cubes. Take turns.

At Your Turn Toss two cubes to find your tables. **EXAMPLE:** Choose the 3rd table on the left and the 5th table on the right, **or** choose the 5th table on the left and the 3rd table on the right. Mark your choices with paper clips.

How to Play Find the expression that belongs at the beginning of the second row in the table on the left. Use the same expression to complete the table you chose on the right. Which three numbers belong on the second row of that table? Find and cover the answer. Lose your turn if the answer is taken.

How to Win The first player or team to get any three connected rectangles in a row or column wins.

Left tables:

n	2	4	6
	4	8	12

n	12	8	4
	6	4	2

n	8	12	16
	2	3	4

n	3	5	7
	9	15	21

n	12	8	4
	6	4	2

n	8	12	16
	2	3	4

Game board:

6, 8, 4	2, 4, 3	16, 32, 24	24, 32, 16
32, 16, 24	4, 8, 6	36, 48, 24	8, 4, 6
24, 48, 36	48, 24, 36	8, 24, 40	3, 4, 2
4, 2, 3	2, 6, 10	12, 36, 60	1, 3, 5

Right tables:

n	12	16	8
	☐	☐	☐

n	16	8	12
	☐	☐	☐

n	4	12	20
	☐	☐	☐

n	8	16	12
	☐	☐	☐

n	4	12	20
	☐	☐	☐

n	16	8	12
	☐	☐	☐

Play again! Talk about your strategies as you play.

Teamwork

Get Started 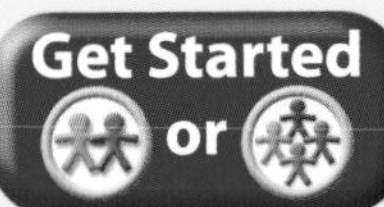

Get paper and a pencil, a ruler, and coordinate grid paper.
Put 1 2 3 4 in a bag.

Repeat for Each Round

Choose **a**, **b**, **c**, **d**, **e**, or **f**.
Pick a tile. Pick two tiles if your group has only two students.
Do the jobs listed below in order.
To find your job, find the number that matches the tile you chose.

 **Read the equation, and the values given for *x*.**

 **Make a table of values for *x* and *y*.**

 **Plot a point for each ordered pair in the table of values.**

 **Connect the points to graph the equation.**

a. $y = x + 1$
Let $x = 0, 1, 2, 3$

b. $y = 3x$
Let $x = 0, 1, 2, 3$

c. $y = x - 2$
Let $x = 2, 3, 4, 5$

d. $y = x + 5$
Let $x = 0, 2, 4, 5$

e. $y = 4x$
Let $x = 0, 1, 2, 3$

f. $y = x - 3$
Let $x = 3, 4, 5, 6$

If you have more time 

Make up an equation. Choose values for *x*. Follow steps 1 – 4 for your equation. Use the values of *x* that you chose.

Teamwork

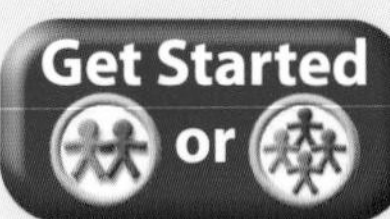

Get paper and a pencil, a ruler, and coordinate grid paper.
Put 1 2 3 4 in a bag.

Repeat for Each Round

Choose **a**, **b**, or **c**.
Pick a tile. Pick two tiles if your group has only two students.
Do the jobs listed below in order.
To find your job, find the number that matches the tile you chose.

 **Plot the three ordered pairs.**

 **Connect the points. Extend the line.**

 **Copy and complete the table. Explain the pattern.**

 **Find the linear equation for the straight line.**

a. Plot and label these points:
E (2, 6), F (4, 8), G (6, 10)

x	y
2	
4	
6	
8	
10	

$y =$ ___

b. Plot and label these points:
H (1, 3), I (2, 6), J (3, 9)

x	y
0	
1	
2	
3	
4	

$y =$ ___

c. Plot and label these points:
K (3, 4), L (4, 5), M (6, 7)

x	y
0	
3	
4	
5	
6	

$y =$ ___

Name four other points that would be on one of these lines.
Repeat for each of the other two lines.

Teamwork

Get Started Get paper and a pencil.
Put 1 2 3 4 in a bag.

Repeat for Each Round Choose **a**, **b**, **c**, **d**, **e**, or **f**.
Pick a tile. Pick two tiles if your group has only two students.
Do the jobs listed below in order.
To find your job, find the number that matches the tile you chose.

 **Read the word phrase. Choose a variable for the unknown amount.**

 **Write that word phrase as an algebraic expression. Use the variable from step 1.**

 **Write that algebraic expression in another way if possible. Use the same variable.**

 **Translate each algebraic expression into words.**

a. 7 more pieces of paper than Matilda has

b. Three times the number of paper clips

c. A number of students divided into 4 teams

d. The current price of the blouse less $10.00

e. Joe was two pounds heavier after the vacation

f. Choices were increased by three

Make up some word phrases.
Follow steps 1 – 4 for your word phrases.

Teamwork

Get paper and a pencil.
Put 1 2 3 4 in a bag.

Repeat for Each Round

Choose **a**, **b**, **c**, **d**, **e**, or **f**.
Pick a tile. Pick two tiles if your group has only two students.
Do the jobs listed below in order.
To find your job, find the number that matches the tile you chose.

1. **Translate the algebraic expression into a word phrase.**
2. **Translate the algebraic expression into a word phrase in a different way.**
3. **Write the algebraic expression in a different way if possible. Use the same variable.**
4. **Describe a situation that you can translate into the algebraic expression if *a* stands for a number of apples.**

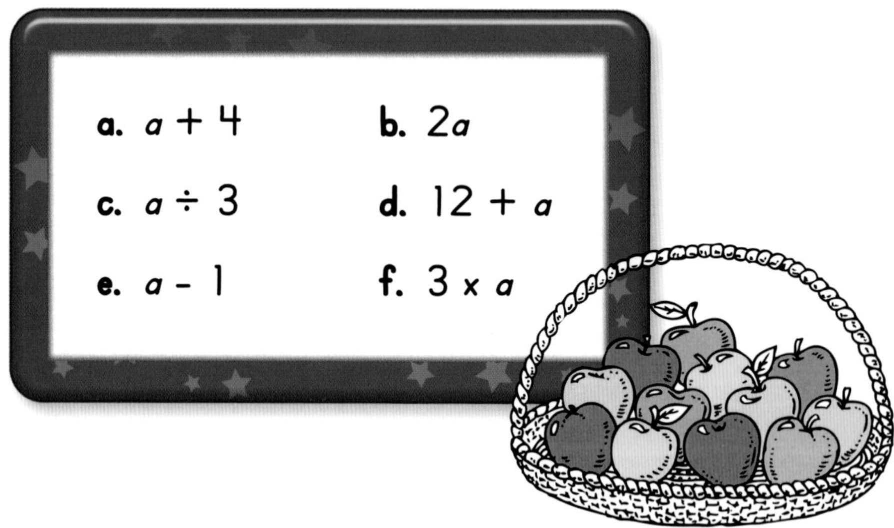

Choose a different value for each variable.
Evaluate an algebraic expression for the value you chose.

Teamwork

Get 40 squares to act out the problems.
Put 1 2 3 4 in a bag.

Repeat for Each Round

Choose **a**, **b**, **c**, or **d**.
Pick a tile. Pick two tiles if your group has only two students.
Do the jobs listed below in order.
To find your job, find the number that matches the tile you chose.

Read the problem to your team.

Tell your team what is known and what you have to find.

Use squares to act out the situation. Work with your team to solve the problem.

Work with your team to solve the problem using a different strategy.

a

Bill has 40 baseball cards. He has 10 New York Yankees cards. He has equal numbers of Chicago Cubs and Boston Red Sox cards. Bill has no other kind of baseball cards. How many cards does he have for each team?

b

Keith's club had a craft sale. They made kites, wood sculptures, and puzzles. They sold 28 items. The club sold twice as many kites as puzzles, and twice as many puzzles as wood sculptures. How many of each did the club sell?

c

Mike's percussion band has 11 members. 2 people play keyboard. Half as many people play the cymbals as the drums. No one plays any other instrument. How many people play the drums?

d

Sally has 33 bears and dolls. She has twice as many bears as dolls. How many of each kind does she have?

Make up a problem that your team members can solve by acting it out with squares.

Teamwork

Get 40 squares to act out the problems.
Put 1 2 3 4 in a bag.

Repeat for Each Round

Choose **a**, **b**, **c**, or **d**.
Pick a tile. Pick two tiles if your group has only two students.
Do the jobs listed below in order.
To find your job, find the number that matches the tile you chose.

Read the information to your team.

Create a question that your team can answer by interpreting the information given.

Use squares to act out the situation. Work with your team to answer the question.

Explain how to use a different strategy to answer the same question or another question.

a

Bill's band has 40 members. 25 are woodwinds. Twice as many play brass instruments as percussion. There are no other types of instruments in the band.

b

Mel's club had a craft sale. They made kites, wood sculptures, and puzzles. They sold 50 items in all. They sold 20 kites, and twice as many puzzles as wood sculptures.

c

Carla spent 12 dollars at the grocery store, 10 dollars at the bakery, and equal amounts of money at the florist and deli. She spent $32 in all.

d

Stan took a survey of the 24 cars on his street. He saw only red cars, black cars, and blue cars. There were 3 red cars, and twice as many black cars as blue cars.

Make up a problem that your team members can solve by acting it out.

Tic Tac Toe

Get Started Get 20 squares in one color and 20 in another color.
Get two number cubes for players to share. Take turns.

For Each Round Toss two cubes. Each number you toss is a factor.
Multiply those numbers to find the product. **Form a fraction with that product as its numerator and 36 as its denominator.**
Find an equivalent fraction on the game board. Explain your choice.
Cover the answer. If the answer is taken, lose your turn.

Example The factors are 3 and 5. Multiply $3 \times 5 = 15$.
The fraction is $\frac{15}{36}$. Find an equivalent fraction, and then explain why those two fractions are equivalent.

How to Win The first player or team to cover a row, column, or diagonal in one of the four sections of the game board wins.

$\frac{2}{18}$	$\frac{1}{12}$	$\frac{3}{6}$	$\frac{3}{9}$	$\frac{4}{18}$	$\frac{10}{18}$
$\frac{6}{18}$	$\frac{2}{3}$	$\frac{2}{72}$	$\frac{5}{6}$	$\frac{1}{2}$	$\frac{2}{12}$
$\frac{2}{9}$	$\frac{1}{4}$	$\frac{3}{18}$	$\frac{5}{18}$	$\frac{9}{9}$	$\frac{50}{72}$
$\frac{4}{9}$	$\frac{10}{18}$	$\frac{2}{24}$	$\frac{5}{9}$	$\frac{5}{12}$	$\frac{6}{6}$
$\frac{1}{18}$	$\frac{1}{6}$	$\frac{10}{12}$	$\frac{2}{4}$	$\frac{1}{9}$	$\frac{8}{18}$
$\frac{4}{12}$	$\frac{3}{12}$	$\frac{4}{6}$	$\frac{2}{8}$	$\frac{10}{72}$	$\frac{1}{3}$

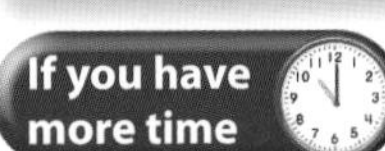

If you have more time Play again!

Tic Tac Toe

Get Started 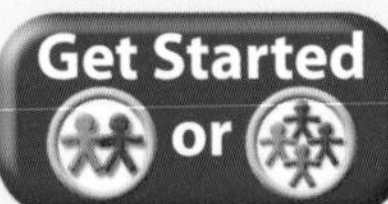 Get 20 squares in one color and 20 in another color. Get two number cubes for players to share. Take turns.

For Each Round Toss two cubes. Each number you toss is a factor. Multiply those numbers to find the product. **Form a fraction with that number as its numerator and 48 as its denominator.** Find an equivalent fraction on the game board. Explain your choice. Cover the answer. If the answer is taken, lose your turn.

Example The factors are 3 and 5. Multiply $3 \times 5 = 15$. The fraction is $\frac{15}{48}$. Find an equivalent fraction, and then explain why those two fractions are equivalent.

How to Win The first player or team to cover a row, column, or diagonal in one of the four sections of the game board wins.

$\frac{10}{16}$	$\frac{5}{16}$	$\frac{1}{8}$	$\frac{2}{4}$	$\frac{3}{18}$	$\frac{3}{16}$
$\frac{5}{12}$	$\frac{1}{3}$	$\frac{2}{96}$	$\frac{6}{16}$	$\frac{1}{4}$	$\frac{1}{24}$
$\frac{3}{8}$	$\frac{3}{4}$	$\frac{5}{24}$	$\frac{1}{12}$	$\frac{2}{6}$	$\frac{10}{96}$
$\frac{2}{8}$	$\frac{1}{16}$	$\frac{10}{24}$	$\frac{5}{8}$	$\frac{9}{24}$	$\frac{12}{16}$
$\frac{15}{72}$	$\frac{1}{2}$	$\frac{2}{12}$	$\frac{4}{12}$	$\frac{1}{6}$	$\frac{4}{8}$
$\frac{50}{96}$	$\frac{6}{32}$	$\frac{2}{16}$	$\frac{10}{32}$	$\frac{2}{24}$	$\frac{4}{16}$

 Play again!

Get 10 squares in one color and 10 in another color.
Get two number cubes. Take turns with another player or team.
Talk about math as you play!

At Your Turn

Toss two number cubes. Add the dots. Find your toss below. Follow the directions. Explain your thinking. Cover the answer. If the answer is taken, lose your turn. Have fun!

Toss	Say the fraction. Explain how to find the simplest form of that fraction.
2	$\frac{18}{30}$
3	$\frac{27}{36}$
4	$\frac{18}{27}$
5	$\frac{15}{35}$
6	$\frac{35}{49}$
7	$\frac{24}{30}$
8	$\frac{40}{48}$
9	$\frac{20}{32}$
10	$\frac{49}{63}$
11	$\frac{20}{36}$
12	$\frac{16}{40}$

$\frac{5}{9}$	$\frac{2}{5}$	$\frac{5}{7}$	$\frac{4}{5}$
$\frac{5}{7}$	$\frac{3}{5}$	$\frac{5}{8}$	$\frac{2}{3}$
$\frac{3}{7}$	$\frac{7}{9}$	$\frac{5}{6}$	$\frac{3}{4}$
$\frac{5}{6}$	$\frac{4}{5}$	$\frac{3}{7}$	$\frac{5}{8}$

How to Win

You win if you are the first to get four connected rectangles, like:

Play again!

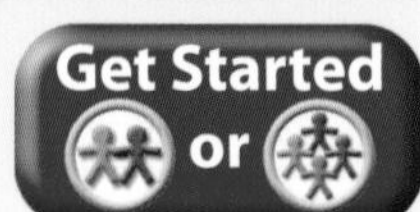

Get 10 squares in one color and 10 in another color.
Get two number cubes. Take turns with another player or team.
Remember, GCF is the greatest common factor.

At Your Turn

Toss two number cubes. Add the dots. Find your toss below. Follow the directions. Explain your thinking. Cover the answer. If the answer is taken, lose your turn. Have fun!

Toss	Find a fraction below that you can simplify with this GCF. Explain how to simplify that fraction.
2	GCF = 9
3	GCF = 4
4	GCF = 3
5	GCF = 5
6	GCF = 6
7	GCF = 7
8	GCF = 8
9	GCF = 3
10	GCF = 2
11	GCF = 4
12	GCF = 9

$\frac{27}{45}$	$\frac{30}{42}$	$\frac{35}{42}$	$\frac{12}{16}$
$\frac{15}{24}$	$\frac{6}{21}$	$\frac{15}{35}$	$\frac{14}{18}$
$\frac{40}{48}$	$\frac{28}{35}$	$\frac{20}{36}$	$\frac{25}{35}$
$\frac{6}{9}$	$\frac{18}{45}$	$\frac{24}{56}$	$\frac{30}{48}$

How to Win

You win if you are the first to get four connected rectangles, like:

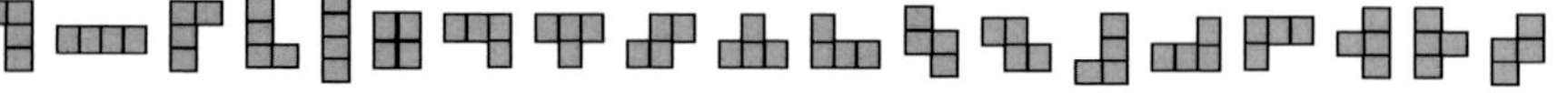

Play again!

Choose a tile. Look at the fraction next to that tile number. Decide if the fraction is less than $\frac{1}{2}$, equal to $\frac{1}{2}$, or greater than $\frac{1}{2}$. Explain your thinking. Stack the tile in the space below your answer. Display each 0–9 tile exactly once. If you have a partner, take turns.

Tile	Fraction	Tile	Fraction	Tile	Fraction	Tile	Fraction
0	$\frac{3}{5}$	1	$\frac{4}{8}$	2	$\frac{7}{12}$	3	$\frac{5}{10}$
4	$\frac{2}{3}$	5	$\frac{7}{16}$	6	$\frac{5}{11}$	7	$\frac{8}{15}$
		8	$\frac{3}{6}$	9	$\frac{5}{12}$		

The fraction is less than $\frac{1}{2}$.	The fraction is equal to $\frac{1}{2}$.	The fraction is greater than $\frac{1}{2}$.

Make up another fraction puzzle like this one.
Ask your partner to stack the number tiles for the fractions in your puzzle.

Choose a tile. Read the addends next to that tile number. Decide if each addend is closer to 0, $\frac{1}{2}$, or 1. Estimate. Decide if the estimate is less than one, equal to one, or greater than one. Stack the tile in the space below your answer. Display each 0–9 tile exactly once. If you have a partner, take turns.

0 $\frac{1}{5} + \frac{3}{8}$ 1 $\frac{2}{3} + \frac{4}{5}$ 2 $\frac{3}{4} + \frac{1}{4}$ 3 $\frac{5}{8} + \frac{3}{6}$

4 $\frac{4}{8} + \frac{3}{7}$ 5 $\frac{1}{12} + \frac{2}{5}$ 6 $\frac{3}{8} + \frac{5}{8}$ 7 $\frac{9}{10} + \frac{6}{7}$

8 $\frac{4}{5} + \frac{2}{3}$ 9 $\frac{3}{7} + \frac{4}{9}$

The estimate is less than one.	The estimate is equal to one.	The estimate is greater than one.

Make up another fraction puzzle like this one. Ask a partner to stack the number tiles for the addends in your puzzle.

Get Started Get 10 squares in one color and 10 in another color, two paper clips, and two number cubes. Get paper and a pencil. Take turns.

At Your Turn Toss two cubes to find your ovals. **EXAMPLE:** ⚂⚄ Choose the 3rd oval on the left and the 5th oval on the right, **or** choose the 5th oval on the left and the 3rd oval on the right. Mark your ovals with paper clips.

How to Play Explain how to compute the least common multiple of the numbers you chose in the left and right ovals. Find and cover the LCM. Lose your turn if the answer is taken.

How to Win The first player or team to get any three connected rectangles in a row or column wins.

Left ovals: 3, 4, 5, 6, 3, 4

21	30	18	9
42	8	24	40
20	10	36	45
28	35	24	30

Right ovals: 7, 8, 9, 10, 8, 9

Play again! This time, say the multiples of each number.

Get 10 squares in one color and 10 in another color, one paper clip, and one number cube. Get paper and a pencil. Take turns.

At Your Turn Toss one cube to find your oval. **EXAMPLE:** Choose the 3rd oval on the left, **or** choose the 3rd oval on the right. Mark your oval with a paper clip.

How to Play The number you choose is a least common multiple. Find two numbers that have the LCM you chose. Explain. Cover the answer. Lose your turn if the answer is taken.

How to Win The first player or team to get any three connected rectangles in a row or column wins.

Left ovals: 10, 90, 24, 16, 32, 12

5, 10	3, 5	8, 12	12, 15
4, 16	8, 32	3, 4	7, 8
5, 18	9, 10	9, 12	12, 48
4, 6	3, 8	6, 7	30, 60

Right ovals: 15, 48, 42, 56, 60, 36

Play again! Talk about your strategy as you play.

Get 10 squares in one color and 10 in another color, two paper clips, and two number cubes. Take turns.

At Your Turn

Toss two cubes to find your ovals. **EXAMPLE:** Choose the 3rd oval on the left and the 5th oval on the right, **or** choose the 5th oval on the left and the 3rd oval on the right. Mark your ovals with paper clips.

How to Play

Explain how to find a common denominator for the two fractions you chose. Find and cover a common denominator.
Lose your turn if the answer is taken.

How to Win

The first player or team to get any three connected rectangles in a row or column wins.

Left ovals: $\frac{1}{2}$, $\frac{1}{4}$, $\frac{1}{3}$, $\frac{1}{6}$, $\frac{1}{4}$, $\frac{1}{3}$

15	36	12	8
18	9	24	20
24	16	10	12
12	18	30	24

Right ovals: $\frac{1}{8}$, $\frac{1}{5}$, $\frac{1}{9}$, $\frac{1}{12}$, $\frac{1}{9}$, $\frac{1}{5}$

Play again! This time, for each fraction in the ovals you choose, explain how to find an equivalent fraction that has the common denominator.

Get Started  Get 10 squares in one color and 10 in another color, one paper clip, and one number cube. Take turns.

At Your Turn Toss one cube to find your oval. **EXAMPLE:** [cube showing 3] Choose the 3rd oval on the left, **or** choose the 3rd oval on the right. Mark your oval with a paper clip.

How to Play Explain how to find a common denominator for $\frac{1}{6}$ and the fraction you chose. Find and cover a common denominator. Lose your turn if the answer is taken.

How to Win The first player or team to get any three connected rectangles in a row or column wins.

Left ovals: $\frac{6}{11}$, $\frac{1}{2}$, $\frac{7}{10}$, $\frac{4}{9}$, $\frac{3}{5}$, $\frac{5}{9}$

18	6	18	66
24	48	30	12
42	18	6	60
12	36	54	24

Right ovals: $\frac{3}{4}$, $\frac{1}{3}$, $\frac{2}{3}$, $\frac{2}{7}$, $\frac{3}{8}$, $\frac{5}{12}$

Play again! Talk about your strategies as you play.

Get Started or

Get 10 squares in one color and 10 in another color. Get two number cubes. Take turns with another player or team. Talk about math as you play!

At Your Turn

Toss two number cubes. Add the dots. Find your toss below. Follow the directions. Explain your thinking. Cover the answer. If the answer is taken, lose your turn. Have fun!

Toss	Get paper and a pencil. Read the fractions. Explain how to add the fractions and how to find the sum in simplest form.
2	$\frac{1}{5} + \frac{1}{2}$
3	$\frac{2}{15} + \frac{3}{5}$
4	$\frac{3}{8} + \frac{1}{10}$
5	$\frac{2}{5} + \frac{1}{4}$
6	$\frac{5}{8} + \frac{1}{6}$
7	$\frac{1}{5} + \frac{1}{3} + \frac{1}{4}$
8	$\frac{2}{6} + \frac{4}{7}$
9	$\frac{3}{8} + \frac{5}{20}$
10	$\frac{2}{11} + \frac{1}{2}$
11	$\frac{1}{5} + \frac{1}{8}$
12	$\frac{3}{10} + \frac{1}{6}$

$\frac{13}{40}$	$\frac{47}{60}$	$\frac{15}{22}$	$\frac{11}{15}$
$\frac{19}{24}$	$\frac{7}{15}$	$\frac{5}{8}$	$\frac{19}{40}$
$\frac{19}{21}$	$\frac{5}{8}$	$\frac{19}{24}$	$\frac{13}{20}$
$\frac{13}{20}$	$\frac{47}{60}$	$\frac{7}{10}$	$\frac{19}{21}$

How to Win

You win if you are the first to get four connected rectangles, like:

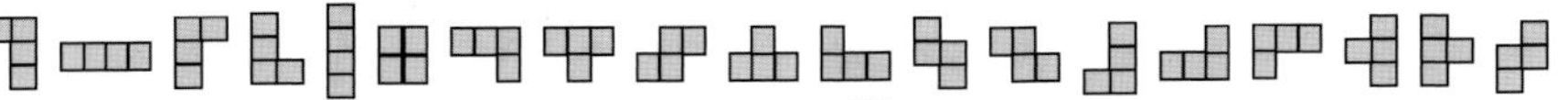

Play again!

Get 10 squares in one color and 10 in another color. Get two number cubes. Take turns with another player or team. Talk about math as you play!

At Your Turn Toss two number cubes. Add the dots. Find your toss below. Follow the directions. Explain your thinking. Cover the answer. If the answer is taken, lose your turn. Have fun!

Toss	Get paper and a pencil. Read the sum. Find two fractions with that sum. Explain your choice.
2	The sum is $\frac{17}{18}$.
3	The sum is $\frac{3}{4}$.
4	The sum is $\frac{13}{16}$.
5	The sum is $\frac{41}{45}$.
6	The sum is $\frac{47}{60}$.
7	The sum is $\frac{7}{8}$.
8	The sum is $\frac{19}{24}$.
9	The sum is $\frac{29}{40}$.
10	The sum is $\frac{23}{24}$.
11	The sum is $\frac{43}{45}$.
12	The sum is $\frac{99}{100}$.

$\frac{7}{12} + \frac{1}{5}$	$\frac{10}{16} + \frac{2}{12}$	$\frac{4}{9} + \frac{7}{15}$	$\frac{5}{9} + \frac{2}{5}$
$\frac{5}{8} + \frac{1}{6}$	$\frac{1}{9} + \frac{5}{6}$	$\frac{1}{8} + \frac{3}{4}$	$\frac{1}{8} + \frac{3}{5}$
$\frac{2}{16} + \frac{6}{8}$	$\frac{1}{16} + \frac{3}{4}$	$\frac{3}{9} + \frac{26}{45}$	$\frac{5}{10} + \frac{1}{4}$
$\frac{20}{30} + \frac{7}{60}$	$\frac{5}{8} + \frac{1}{10}$	$\frac{73}{100} + \frac{13}{50}$	$\frac{7}{8} + \frac{1}{12}$

How to Win You win if you are the first to get four connected rectangles, like:

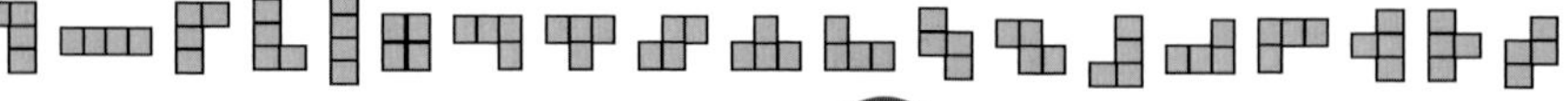

Play again!

Get Started  Get 10 squares in one color and 10 in another color, two paper clips, and two number cubes. Take turns.

At Your Turn Toss two cubes to find your ovals. **EXAMPLE:** Choose the 3rd oval on the left and the 5th oval on the right, **or** choose the 5th oval on the left and the 3rd oval on the right. Mark your ovals with paper clips.

How to Play Explain how to subtract the fraction you chose on the right from the fraction you chose on the left. Find and cover the difference. Lose your turn if the answer is taken.

How to Win The first player or team to get any three connected rectangles in a row or column wins.

Left ovals: $\frac{7}{10}$, $\frac{3}{4}$, $\frac{4}{5}$, $\frac{7}{12}$, $\frac{3}{4}$, $\frac{4}{5}$

$\frac{1}{5}$	$\frac{1}{4}$	$\frac{5}{12}$	$\frac{3}{10}$
$\frac{7}{15}$	$\frac{11}{30}$	$\frac{1}{12}$	$\frac{23}{40}$
$\frac{5}{8}$	$\frac{11}{60}$	$\frac{1}{4}$	$\frac{11}{24}$
$\frac{3}{10}$	$\frac{2}{5}$	$\frac{27}{40}$	$\frac{7}{20}$

Right ovals: $\frac{1}{2}$, $\frac{1}{3}$, $\frac{2}{5}$, $\frac{1}{8}$, $\frac{2}{5}$, $\frac{1}{3}$

If you have more time 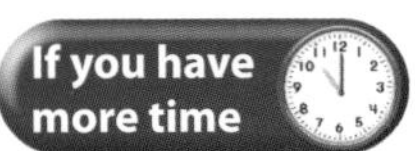 Play again! This time, tell how you know that the fraction in the left oval is greater than the fraction in the right oval.

Get Started  Get 10 squares in one color and 10 in another color, one paper clip, and one number cube. Take turns.

At Your Turn Toss one cube to find your oval. **EXAMPLE:** Choose the 3rd oval on the left, **or** choose the 3rd oval on the right. Mark your oval with a paper clip.

How to Play Explain how to find the difference of the fractions you chose. Is the difference close to 0, close to $\frac{1}{2}$, or close to 1? Find and cover the answer. Lose your turn if the answer is taken.

How to Win The first player or team to get any three connected rectangles in a row or column wins.

Left ovals:

1. $\frac{3}{4} - \frac{1}{3}$
2. $\frac{9}{10} - \frac{1}{5}$
3. $\frac{4}{5} - \frac{1}{10}$
4. $\frac{1}{2} - \frac{3}{8}$
5. $\frac{5}{8} - \frac{1}{6}$
6. $\frac{7}{8} - \frac{1}{16}$

Close to 1	Close to $\frac{1}{2}$	Close to 0	Close to 1
Close to 0	Close to 0	Close to $\frac{1}{2}$	Close to 0
Close to $\frac{1}{2}$	Close to 1	Close to $\frac{1}{2}$	Close to 1
Close to 1	Close to 0	Close to $\frac{1}{2}$	Close to 1

Right ovals:

1. $\frac{4}{5} - \frac{3}{4}$
2. $\frac{1}{8} - \frac{1}{9}$
3. $\frac{7}{8} - \frac{5}{6}$
4. $\frac{3}{10} - \frac{1}{4}$
5. $\frac{4}{8} - \frac{1}{8}$
6. $\frac{11}{12} - \frac{1}{6}$

Play again! Talk about your strategies as you play.

Put 1 2 3 4 in a bag.
Get paper and a pencil.

For Each Round

Choose A, B, C, D, E, or F. Read the directions.
Pick a tile. Pick two tiles if your group has only two students.
Explain how to find the sum or difference of the fractions that are next to the number you chose.
Discuss Which three problems have the same answer?
Decide Which problem has a different answer?

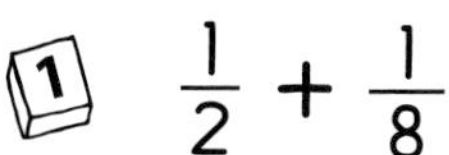

A	Find the sum or the difference
1	$\frac{1}{2} + \frac{1}{8}$
2	$\frac{3}{4} - \frac{1}{8}$
3	$\frac{1}{4} + \frac{3}{8}$
4	$\frac{7}{16} + \frac{1}{4}$

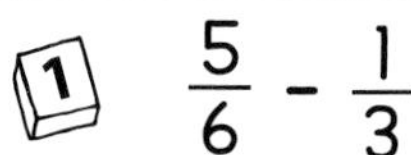

B	Find the sum or the difference
1	$\frac{5}{6} - \frac{1}{3}$
2	$\frac{3}{5} - \frac{1}{10}$
3	$\frac{8}{10} - \frac{1}{5}$
4	$\frac{1}{6} + \frac{1}{3}$

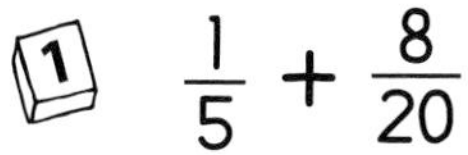

C	Find the sum or the difference
1	$\frac{1}{5} + \frac{8}{20}$
2	$\frac{9}{10} - \frac{1}{5}$
3	$\frac{17}{20} - \frac{1}{4}$
4	$\frac{1}{3} + \frac{4}{15}$

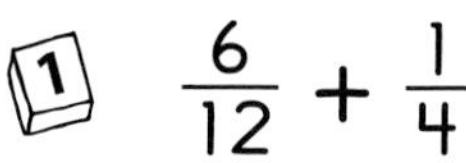

D	Find the sum or the difference
1	$\frac{6}{12} + \frac{1}{4}$
2	$\frac{2}{3} + \frac{1}{12}$
3	$\frac{4}{5} - \frac{1}{10}$
4	$\frac{19}{20} - \frac{1}{5}$

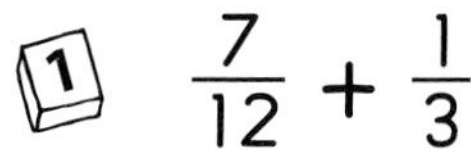

E	Find the sum or the difference
1	$\frac{7}{12} + \frac{1}{3}$
2	$\frac{23}{24} - \frac{1}{8}$
3	$\frac{17}{18} - \frac{1}{9}$
4	$\frac{2}{3} + \frac{1}{6}$

F	Find the sum or the difference
1	$\frac{11}{12} - \frac{1}{4}$
2	$\frac{5}{9} + \frac{1}{3}$
3	$\frac{13}{15} - \frac{1}{5}$
4	$\frac{1}{6} + \frac{1}{2}$

Make up a "Think Together" activity like A, B, C, D, E, or F above. Challenge your classmates to think together to complete your activity.

Put 1 2 3 4 in a bag.
Get paper and a pencil.

For Each Round

Choose **A, B, C, D, E,** or **F**. Simplify the expression.
Pick a tile. Pick two tiles if your group has only two students.
Explain how to simplify the expression that is next to the number you chose.
Discuss Which three expressions have the same value?
Decide Which expression has a different value?

A Simplify the expression.

1	$(\frac{1}{2} + \frac{1}{3}) - \frac{1}{6}$
2	$(\frac{11}{12} - \frac{3}{4}) + \frac{1}{2}$
3	$(\frac{13}{15} - \frac{3}{5}) + \frac{2}{5}$
4	$(\frac{1}{6} + \frac{5}{12}) + \frac{1}{4}$

B Simplify the expression.

1	$(\frac{3}{10} - \frac{3}{20}) + \frac{9}{20}$
2	$(\frac{10}{20} - \frac{3}{10}) + \frac{2}{5}$
3	$(\frac{1}{2} + \frac{3}{10}) - \frac{1}{5}$
4	$(\frac{11}{15} - \frac{1}{3}) + \frac{1}{15}$

C Simplify the expression.

1	$(\frac{2}{3} + \frac{1}{4}) - \frac{5}{6}$
2	$(\frac{1}{2} + \frac{1}{4}) - \frac{1}{8}$
3	$(\frac{9}{16} + \frac{1}{8}) - \frac{1}{16}$
4	$(\frac{3}{4} - \frac{3}{8}) + \frac{1}{4}$

D Simplify the expression.

1	$(\frac{7}{12} - \frac{1}{3}) + \frac{1}{2}$
2	$(\frac{1}{4} + \frac{1}{3}) + \frac{1}{6}$
3	$(\frac{11}{16} - \frac{5}{8}) + \frac{1}{2}$
4	$(\frac{1}{2} + \frac{1}{3}) - \frac{1}{12}$

E Simplify the expression.

1	$(\frac{7}{10} + \frac{1}{5}) - \frac{2}{5}$
2	$(\frac{5}{6} - \frac{2}{3}) + \frac{1}{3}$
3	$(\frac{3}{4} - \frac{1}{3}) + \frac{1}{12}$
4	$(\frac{2}{7} + \frac{5}{14}) - \frac{1}{2}$

F Simplify the expression.

1	$(\frac{2}{3} - \frac{1}{4}) + \frac{1}{6}$
2	$(\frac{1}{4} + \frac{5}{12}) + \frac{1}{6}$
3	$(\frac{11}{18} - \frac{1}{3}) + \frac{5}{9}$
4	$(\frac{17}{24} - \frac{3}{8}) + \frac{1}{2}$

Make up a "Think Together" activity like **A, B, C, D, E,** or **F** above.
Challenge your classmates to think together to complete your activity.

Teamwork

Get paper and a pencil.
Put 1 2 3 4 in a bag.

Repeat for Each Round

Choose **a**, **b**, **c**, or **d**.
Pick a tile. Pick two tiles if your group has only two students.
Do the jobs listed below in order.
To find your job, find the number that matches the tile you chose.

Read the problem to your team. Draw a picture to show your team what you know and what you need to find.

Write an equation that can be used to solve the problem.

Work with your team to solve the problem.

Check the answer. Tell your team why the answer is correct or why it needs to be revised.

a. Helen connected a wire extension that is $\frac{1}{2}$ of a foot long to another wire that is $\frac{5}{6}$ of a foot long. How long is the wire with the extension?

b. Mark and Mike baked cookies. Mark used $\frac{7}{8}$ pound of cookie dough. Mike used $\frac{1}{3}$ pound of cookie dough. How much more dough did Mark use?

c. Runner A ran $\frac{1}{3}$ of a mile. Runner B ran $\frac{1}{4}$ of a mile. How much farther did Runner A run than Runner B?

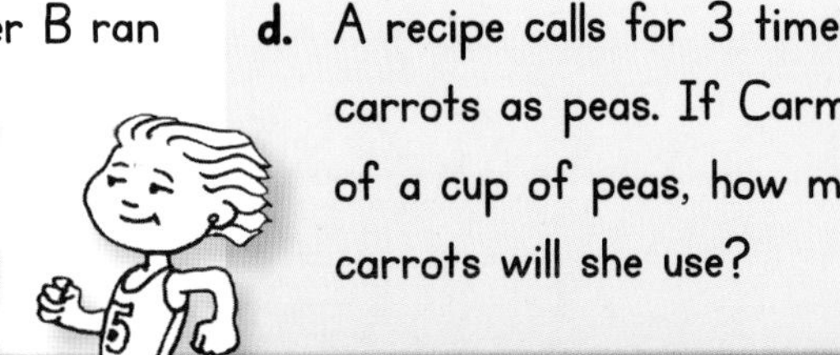

d. A recipe calls for 3 times as many carrots as peas. If Carmen uses $\frac{1}{3}$ of a cup of peas, how many cups of carrots will she use?

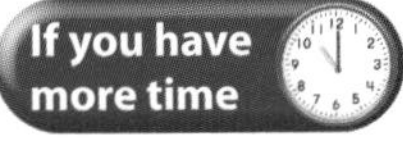

Choose **a**, **b**, **c**, or **d**. Change one fraction in the problem.
Follow steps 1–4 for your new problem.

Teamwork

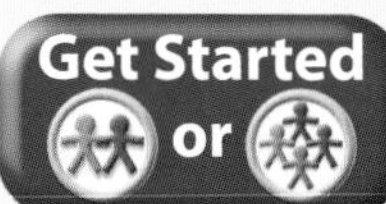

Get paper and a pencil.
Put 1 2 3 4 in a bag.

Repeat for Each Round

Choose **a**, **b**, **c**, or **d**.
Pick a tile. Pick two tiles if your group has only two students.
Do the jobs listed below in order.
To find your job, find the number that matches the tile you chose.

 **Read the question to your team. Decide as a team whether you will draw a picture, write an equation, or both.**

 **Work with your team to answer the question by using the strategy your team chose.**

 **Check the answer. Tell your team why the answer is correct or why it needs to be revised.**

 **Discuss how the answer would change if each runner ran an extra $\frac{1}{4}$ of a mile.**

Runner	Distance Run (miles)
Mark	$\frac{1}{2}$
Betty	$\frac{3}{4}$
Harry	$\frac{7}{8}$

a. How much farther did Betty run than Mark?

b. How many miles in all did these three students run?

c. How much farther did Harry run than Mark?

d. How much farther did Harry run than Betty?

Ask a different question that your team members can answer by using the data in the table.

Display the Digits

0 1 2 3 4 5 6 7 8 9

Explain how to find each missing digit.
Display each 0 – 9 tile exactly once.
If you have a partner, take turns.

a. $\frac{\square}{3} = 1\frac{2}{3}$

b. $\square\frac{3}{4} = \frac{15}{4}$

c. $2\frac{\square}{4} = \frac{9}{4}$

d. $1\frac{1}{5} = \frac{\square}{5}$

e. $3\frac{\square}{11} = \frac{42}{11}$

f. $\frac{59}{7} = \square\frac{3}{7}$

g. $\frac{23}{5} = \square\frac{3}{5}$

h. $5\frac{\square}{9} = \frac{47}{9}$

i. $\frac{31}{8} = 3\frac{\square}{8}$

j. $\frac{18}{3} = 6\frac{\square}{3}$

Make up other puzzles with improper fractions and mixed numbers.
Ask your partner to display the answers with 0 – 9 tiles.

Display the Digits

0 1 2 3 4 5 6 7 8 9

Explain how to find each missing digit.
Display each 0 – 9 tile exactly once.
If you have a partner, take turns.

a. $\frac{44}{10} = 4\frac{\square}{5}$

b. $\square\,\frac{3}{4} = \frac{46}{8}$

c. $\frac{\square}{3} = 2\frac{2}{3}$

d. $2\frac{\square}{8} = \frac{38}{16}$

e. $1\frac{3}{\square} = \frac{20}{14}$

f. $\frac{76}{20} = 3\frac{\square}{5}$

g. $\frac{32}{6} = 5\frac{\square}{3}$

h. $2\frac{5}{\square} = \frac{51}{18}$

i. $1\frac{4}{5} = \frac{\square}{5}$

j. $\frac{56}{7} = 8\frac{\square}{7}$

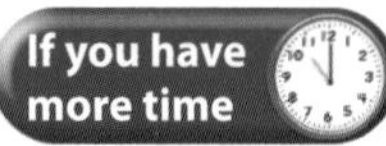

Make up other puzzles with improper fractions and mixed numbers.
Ask your partner to display the answers with 0 – 9 tiles.

Quick Questions

Each player tosses two number cubes.
If your numbers match another player's numbers, toss again.
Decide who will read the first question. Take turns.

For Each Question

Listen to the reader. Discuss and agree on the correct answer.
Every player who has that answer can remove one cube that shows the answer.

How to Win

The first player who removes both cubes wins. Have fun!

a	Estimate the sum of $3\frac{5}{8}$ and $1\frac{1}{4}$.
b	Estimate the difference between $16\frac{2}{3}$ and $14\frac{5}{6}$.
c	Estimate the difference between $12\frac{1}{8}$ and $9\frac{2}{7}$.
d	Estimate the sum of $1\frac{2}{3}$ and $3\frac{7}{9}$.
e	Estimate the sum of $2\frac{1}{5}$ and $3\frac{2}{9}$.
f	Estimate the difference between $24\frac{1}{3}$ and $22\frac{6}{7}$.
g	$53\frac{1}{9}$ is about how much more than $50\frac{4}{5}$?
h	Estimate the sum of $2\frac{5}{7}$ and $1\frac{2}{5}$.
i	Estimate the difference between $37\frac{1}{4}$ and $35\frac{5}{6}$.
j	Estimate the sum of $3\frac{3}{4}$ and $2\frac{1}{5}$.
k	$23\frac{5}{8}$ is about how much less than $26\frac{8}{9}$?
l	Estimate the sum of $3\frac{1}{3}$ and $\frac{4}{7}$.
m	Estimate the sum of $5\frac{3}{5}$ and $\frac{2}{9}$.

n	Estimate the sum of $1\frac{3}{8}$ and $\frac{8}{9}$.
o	Estimate the difference between $40\frac{1}{8}$ and $35\frac{2}{3}$.
p	Estimate the sum of $3\frac{2}{9}$ and $2\frac{1}{4}$.
q	$9\frac{6}{7}$ is about how much more than $7\frac{2}{5}$?
r	Estimate the sum of $\frac{4}{7}$ and $\frac{3}{8}$.
s	Estimate the sum of $5\frac{1}{5}$ and $\frac{1}{7}$.
t	$82\frac{7}{8}$ is about how much less than $85\frac{3}{5}$?
u	Estimate the difference between $12\frac{1}{6}$ and $9\frac{5}{9}$.
v	Estimate the sum of $2\frac{5}{7}$ and $2\frac{7}{8}$.
w	$24\frac{6}{7}$ is about how much more than $23\frac{7}{9}$?
x	Estimate the sum of $2\frac{1}{6}$ and $1\frac{5}{8}$.
y	$16\frac{3}{5}$ is about how much less than $20\frac{1}{8}$?
z	Estimate the sum of $1\frac{1}{5}$ and $4\frac{7}{9}$.

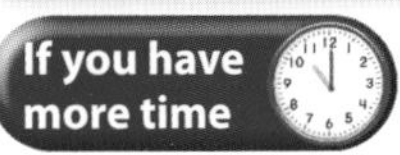

Toss two number cubes again. Play another game.
Begin with the next question in the list.

Quick Questions

Each player tosses two number cubes.
If your numbers match another player's numbers, toss again.
Decide who will read the first question. Take turns.

For Each Question Listen to the reader. Explain how to estimate each sum or difference. Discuss and agree on an answer. Every player who has the answer can remove one cube that shows the answer.

How to Win The first player who removes both cubes wins. Have fun!

a	Estimate the sum of $2\frac{27}{52}$ and $2\frac{19}{42}$.	n	Estimate the sum of $2\frac{45}{87}$ and $2\frac{32}{59}$.
b	Estimate the difference between $19\frac{14}{29}$ and $17\frac{52}{53}$.	o	$7\frac{12}{23}$ is about how much more than $6\frac{49}{75}$?
c	Estimate the sum of $5\frac{21}{46}$ and $1\frac{13}{29}$.	p	Estimate the sum of $1\frac{34}{65}$ and $1\frac{34}{69}$.
d	Estimate the sum of $1\frac{18}{29}$ and $2\frac{47}{95}$.	q	$12\frac{28}{53}$ is about how much less than $14\frac{17}{38}$?
e	$5\frac{31}{50}$ is about how much more than $3\frac{66}{83}$?	r	Estimate the difference between $21\frac{29}{55}$ and $17\frac{18}{33}$.
f	$5\frac{13}{22}$ is about how much less than $12\frac{29}{66}$?	s	Estimate the sum of $1\frac{43}{80}$ and $1\frac{56}{93}$.
g	Estimate the sum of $3\frac{43}{78}$ and $\frac{36}{87}$.	t	Estimate the difference between $4\frac{30}{59}$ and $1\frac{19}{34}$.
h	Estimate the difference between $9\frac{16}{31}$ and $7\frac{16}{33}$.	u	$11\frac{15}{28}$ is about how much more than $9\frac{23}{49}$?
i	$4\frac{38}{73}$ is about how much more than $2\frac{26}{50}$?	v	$22\frac{31}{57}$ is about how much less than $24\frac{46}{89}$?
j	Estimate the sum of $1\frac{19}{42}$ and $3\frac{22}{37}$.	w	Estimate the difference between $3\frac{14}{29}$ and $2\frac{36}{73}$.
k	$5\frac{45}{92}$ is about how much less than $6\frac{12}{25}$?	x	$7\frac{24}{47}$ is about how much more than $2\frac{44}{85}$?
l	Estimate the sum of $1\frac{17}{28}$ and $1\frac{17}{35}$.	y	Estimate the sum of $1\frac{23}{48}$ and $3\frac{38}{75}$.
m	Estimate the difference between $18\frac{31}{55}$ and $14\frac{23}{48}$.	z	$5\frac{29}{60}$ is about how much less than $10\frac{42}{81}$?

Play another game. Begin with the next question in the list. Or make up your own questions like these. Play the game with your questions.

Teamwork

Get paper and a pencil.
Put 1 2 3 4 in a bag. Take turns.

Repeat for Each Round

Pick a number tile. Read the expression next to that number. Find the picture below that matches your expression. Explain why you chose that picture. Decide on the correct sum or difference. Simplify if possible. Use the picture to explain why your answer is correct.

1 $2\frac{3}{5} + 1\frac{1}{5}$ 2 $2\frac{1}{3} - 1\frac{2}{3}$ 3 $2\frac{3}{8} - 1\frac{5}{8}$ 4 $2\frac{3}{4} + 1\frac{3}{4}$

a 

b 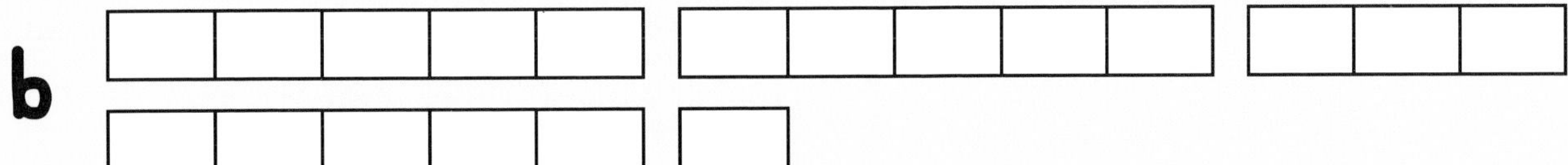

c 

d 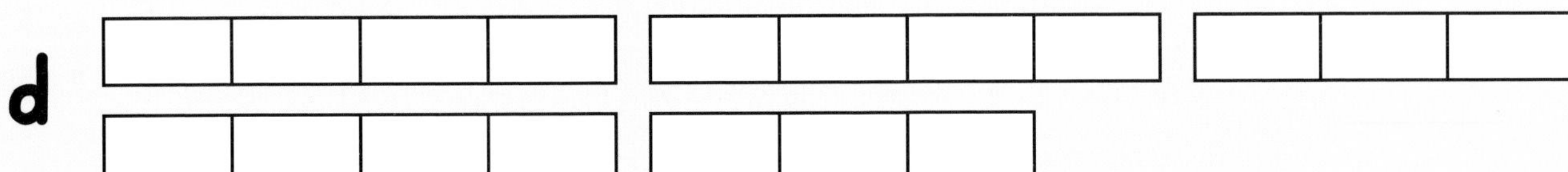

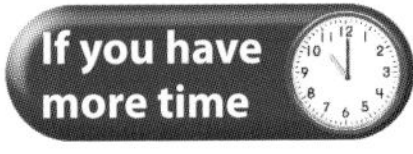

Create an expression with mixed numbers that your team can solve by drawing a picture of fraction strips.

Teamwork

Get paper and a pencil.
Put 1 2 3 4 in a bag. Take turns.

Repeat for Each Round

Pick a number tile. Read the expression next to that number.
Find the picture below that matches your expression. Explain why you chose that picture. Decide on the correct sum or difference.
Simplify if possible. Use the picture to explain why your answer is correct.

1 $1\frac{1}{2} + 2\frac{7}{8}$ 2 $2\frac{1}{2} - 1\frac{1}{4}$ 3 $2\frac{5}{9} - 1\frac{2}{3}$ 4 $1\frac{1}{6} + 2\frac{1}{3}$

a

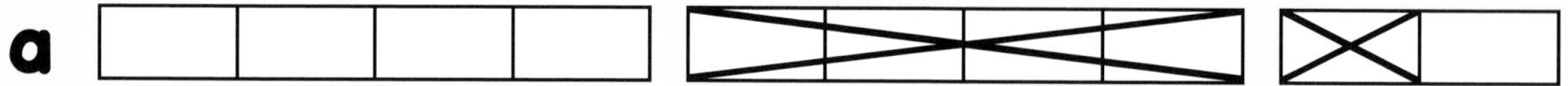

b

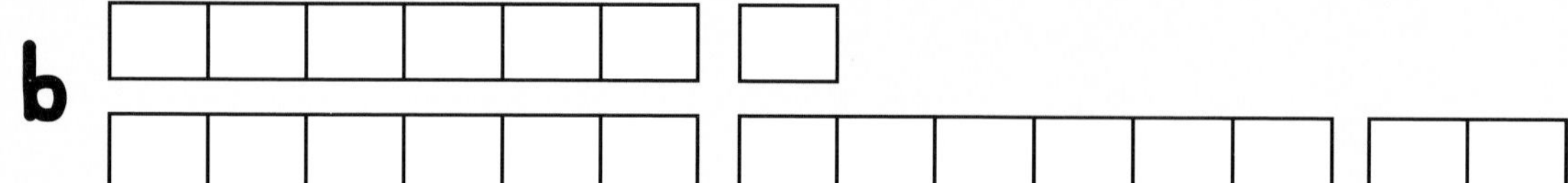

c

d

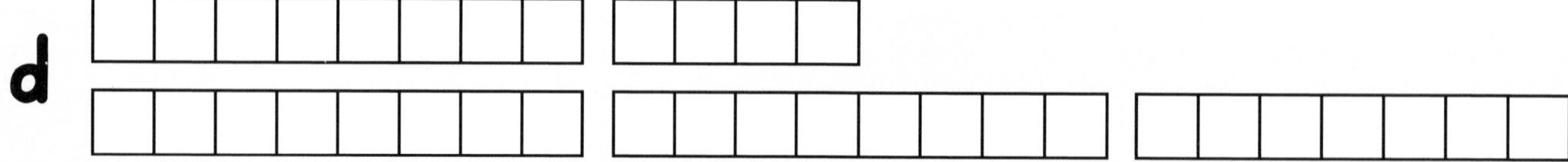

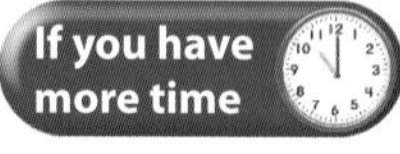

Create an expression with mixed numbers that your team can solve by drawing a picture of fraction strips.

Display the Digits

0 1 2 3 4 5 6 7 8 9

Explain how to compute with mental math to find the sum.
Display each 0–9 tile exactly once. If you have a partner, take turns.

$$1\frac{1}{2} + 3\frac{1}{3} = 4\frac{\boxed{a}}{\boxed{b}}$$

$$9\frac{1}{2} + 5\frac{1}{6} = 14\frac{\boxed{c}}{\boxed{d}}$$

$$12\frac{3}{4} + 9\frac{3}{8} = 22\frac{1}{\boxed{e}}$$

$$4\frac{1}{2} + 4\frac{5}{10} = \boxed{f}$$

$$15\frac{1}{7} + 5\frac{3}{7} = 20\frac{\boxed{g}}{\boxed{h}}$$

$$11\frac{1}{2} + 10\frac{3}{5} = 22\frac{1}{\boxed{i}\boxed{j}}$$

a	b	c	d	e
f	g	h	i	j

Make up another addition puzzle with mixed numbers.
Ask your partner to display the answers with 0–9 tiles.

Display the Digits

0 1 2 3 4 5 6 7 8 9

Explain how to find each missing digit. Use mental math.
Display each 0–9 tile exactly once. If you have a partner, take turns.

$$5\frac{a}{4} + 21\frac{3}{8} = 2b\frac{5}{c}$$

$$d\frac{4}{9} + 5\frac{e}{3} = 13\frac{1}{f}$$

$$1\frac{3}{1g} + 32\frac{4}{h} = 3i\frac{1}{10}$$

$$1\frac{1}{2} + 1\frac{2}{4} = j$$

a	b	c	d	e
f	g	h	i	j

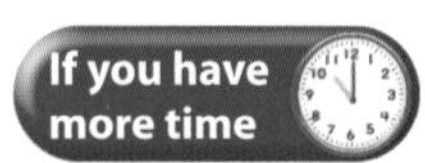

Make up another addition puzzle with mixed numbers.
Ask your partner to display the answers with 0–9 tiles.

Teamwork

Get paper and a pencil.
Put 1 2 3 4 in a bag.

Repeat for Each Round

Choose **A, B, C, D, E,** or **F.**
Pick a tile. Pick two tiles if your group has only two students. Do the jobs listed below in order. To find your job, find the number that matches the tile you chose.

 **Read the subtraction problem to your team.**

 **Decide whether or not you will need to rename the first number. Tell your group how you know.**

 **Work with your team to subtract the numbers. Simplify the difference, if necessary. Make sure everyone has the same answer.**

 **Explain why the answer is reasonable.**

a $5 - 1\frac{2}{3}$	**b** $4\frac{1}{3} - 1\frac{3}{4}$	**c** $2\frac{1}{6} - 1\frac{1}{2}$
d $8\frac{3}{4} - 2\frac{1}{6}$	**e** $6 - 3\frac{1}{3}$	**f** $7\frac{5}{8} - 2\frac{1}{6}$

Make up a subtraction problem with mixed numbers.
Ask your team to complete steps 1–4 for your problem.

Teamwork

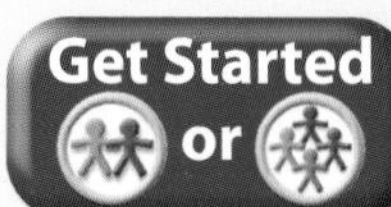

Get paper and a pencil.
Put 1 2 3 4 in a bag.

Repeat for Each Round

Choose **A, B, C, D, E,** or **F.**
Pick a tile. Pick two tiles if your group has only two students. Do the jobs listed below in order. To find your job, find the number that matches the tile you chose.

 **Read the subtraction problem to your team.**

 **Explain how to estimate the difference of the two mixed numbers.**

 **Work with your team to compute the exact difference. Simplify the difference, if necessary. Make sure everyone has the same answer.**

 **Compare the estimate and the exact answer. Explain why the answer is reasonable.**

a $8\frac{1}{3} - 2\frac{3}{4}$	b $12\frac{2}{5} - 4\frac{1}{2}$	c $7\frac{3}{8} - 1\frac{3}{4}$
d $5\frac{1}{2} - 2\frac{3}{4}$	e $9\frac{7}{10} - 3\frac{3}{10}$	f $11\frac{4}{9} - 1\frac{1}{3}$

Make up a subtraction problem with mixed numbers.
Ask your team to complete steps 1–4 for your problem.

Get 10 squares in one color and 10 in another color.
Get two number cubes. Take turns with another player or team.
Talk about math as you play!

At Your Turn

Toss two number cubes. Add the dots. Find your toss below.
Follow the directions. Explain your thinking. Cover the answer.
If the answer is taken, lose your turn. Have fun!

Toss	Read the expression. Explain how to add or subtract. Simplify the expression.
2	$1\frac{5}{8} + 2\frac{1}{4}$
3	$4\frac{5}{9} - 2\frac{1}{3}$
4	$2\frac{2}{3} + 1\frac{4}{9}$
5	$4\frac{3}{8} - 1\frac{3}{4}$
6	$1\frac{1}{3} + 2\frac{3}{4}$
7	$4\frac{1}{2} - 1\frac{2}{3}$
8	$4\frac{2}{5} - 2\frac{1}{2}$
9	$1\frac{5}{6} + 2\frac{2}{3}$
10	$3\frac{1}{4} - 1\frac{1}{2}$
11	$2\frac{7}{10} + 1\frac{1}{5}$
12	$3\frac{5}{6} - 1\frac{1}{3}$

$2\frac{5}{8}$	$4\frac{1}{9}$	$2\frac{1}{2}$	$2\frac{5}{6}$
$1\frac{3}{4}$	$1\frac{9}{10}$	$4\frac{1}{12}$	$3\frac{7}{8}$
$2\frac{2}{9}$	$2\frac{5}{6}$	$4\frac{1}{2}$	$3\frac{9}{10}$
$4\frac{1}{12}$	$4\frac{1}{2}$	$2\frac{5}{8}$	$1\frac{9}{10}$

How to Win

You win if you are the first to get four connected rectangles, like:

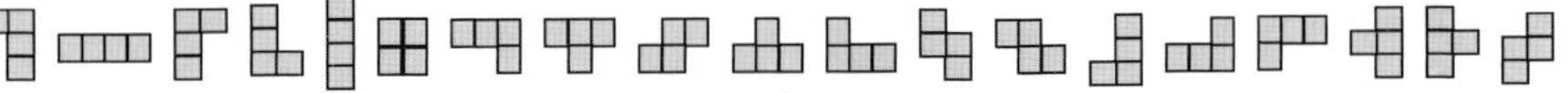

Play again!

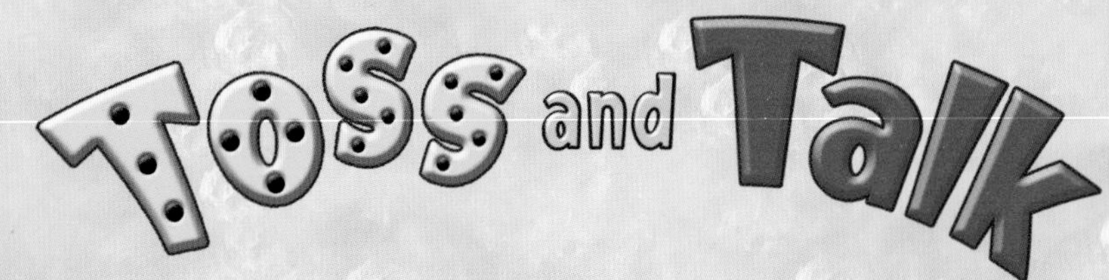

Get 10 squares in one color and 10 in another color.
Get two number cubes. Take turns with another player or team.
Talk about math as you play!

At Your Turn

Toss two number cubes. Add the dots. Find your toss below.
Follow the directions. Explain your thinking. Cover the answer.
If the answer is taken, lose your turn. Have fun!

Toss	Read the expression. Explain how to add or subtract. Simplify the expression.
2	$4\frac{1}{3} - 2\frac{5}{6}$
3	$2\frac{3}{4} + 1\frac{2}{3}$
4	$(1\frac{1}{3} + 1\frac{1}{4}) + 2\frac{7}{12}$
5	$(3\frac{5}{8} + 1\frac{1}{2}) - 2\frac{1}{4}$
6	$(4\frac{4}{5} - 2\frac{1}{2}) + 1\frac{3}{10}$
7	$(2\frac{2}{3} + 2\frac{3}{4}) - 2\frac{1}{2}$
8	$(5\frac{7}{8} - 1\frac{3}{4}) - 1\frac{5}{8}$
9	$(2\frac{1}{3} + 2\frac{1}{6}) - 2\frac{5}{6}$
10	$(1\frac{1}{2} + 2\frac{1}{4}) + 1\frac{3}{4}$
11	$4\frac{1}{2} - 1\frac{3}{5}$
12	$2\frac{3}{5} + 1\frac{7}{10}$

$2\frac{7}{8}$	$2\frac{9}{10}$	$1\frac{2}{3}$	$3\frac{3}{5}$
$5\frac{1}{2}$	$2\frac{1}{2}$	$2\frac{11}{12}$	$1\frac{1}{2}$
$4\frac{3}{10}$	$3\frac{3}{5}$	$1\frac{2}{3}$	$5\frac{1}{6}$
$2\frac{11}{12}$	$2\frac{7}{8}$	$4\frac{5}{12}$	$2\frac{1}{2}$

You win if you are the first to get four connected rectangles, like:

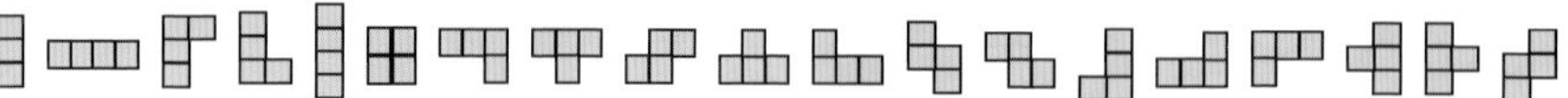

Play again!

Teamwork

Get paper and a pencil.
Put 1 2 3 4 5 6 7 in a bag. Take turns.

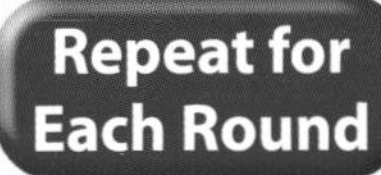

Pick a number tile. Read the problem next to that number.
Find the picture below that helps you to solve the problem.
Explain why the picture matches the problem.
Ask your team to choose an operation, and to solve the problem.
Decide if the answer is correct. Cover the picture with your tile.

Mary saved $\frac{1}{2}$ of her babysitting money. She spent $\frac{1}{4}$ of her babysitting money on clothes. What fraction is left for other things?

John gives $\frac{1}{8}$ of a pizza to his sister and $\frac{1}{4}$ to his brother. What fraction of the pizza did John give away?

Alice gives $\frac{1}{4}$ of a cup of popcorn to Bob and $\frac{5}{8}$ of a cup to Sue. What fraction of the cup is left for Alice?

Sam needs $\frac{3}{4}$ of a gallon of paint. He has $\frac{3}{8}$ of a gallon. How much more paint does Sam need?

John plants $\frac{2}{5}$ of the family farm. Harold plants another $\frac{1}{5}$ and Barry another $\frac{1}{10}$. What fraction of the farm did they plant?

Half of the class visited the zoo, $\frac{5}{16}$ of the class visited the park. The rest went to the museum. What fraction of the class went to the museum?

June has 10 hours to spend on her day off. June spends $\frac{1}{5}$ of her day off at the beach, $\frac{1}{10}$ of the day at the gym, and $\frac{3}{10}$ of the day shopping. What fraction of her day off was spent on these three activities?

?		
$\frac{2}{5}$	$\frac{1}{5}$	$\frac{1}{10}$

1		
$\frac{1}{2}$	$\frac{5}{16}$	?

1		
$\frac{1}{4}$	$\frac{1}{2}$	?

?	
$\frac{1}{8}$	$\frac{1}{4}$

$\frac{3}{4}$	
$\frac{3}{8}$	?

1		
$\frac{1}{4}$	$\frac{5}{8}$	?

?		
$\frac{1}{5}$	$\frac{1}{10}$	$\frac{3}{10}$

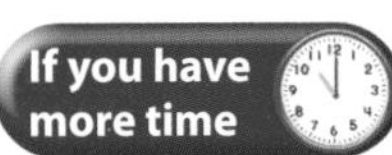

Make up your own problem that involves adding or subtracting fractions.
Ask your partner to draw a picture for it.

Teamwork

Get Started or

Get paper and a pencil.
Put 0 1 2 3 4 5 6 7 8 9 in a bag. Take turns.

Repeat for Each Round

Pick a number tile. Find the picture next to that number.
Create a real-world problem represented by the picture. Ask your team members to choose an operation and solve your problem. Explain why the answer is reasonable. Use your tile to cover the answer.

0

n miles	
$\frac{1}{2}$ of a mile	$\frac{3}{4}$ of a mile

1

$1\frac{5}{8}$ inches	
$\frac{7}{16}$ of an inch	*n* inches

2

n boxes	
$1\frac{3}{8}$ boxes	$2\frac{1}{2}$ boxes

3

$1\frac{7}{8}$ quarts	
$\frac{3}{4}$ of a quart	*n* quarts

4

$1\frac{1}{5}$ miles	
$\frac{3}{10}$ of a mile	*n* of a mile

5

n inches	
$1\frac{3}{4}$ inches	$\frac{7}{8}$ of an inch

6

$1\frac{3}{5}$ pounds	
$\frac{3}{10}$ of a pound	*n* pounds

7

$1\frac{1}{2}$ boxes	
$\frac{1}{4}$ of a box	*n* boxes

8

3 quarts	
$\frac{3}{4}$ of a quart	*n* quarts

9

n cans		
$\frac{1}{2}$ of a can	$1\frac{3}{4}$ cans	$\frac{7}{8}$ of a can

$n = 3\frac{7}{8}$	$n = 3\frac{1}{8}$	$n = 2\frac{5}{8}$	$n = 1\frac{1}{4}$	$n = 1\frac{1}{8}$
$n = 2\frac{1}{4}$	$n = 1\frac{3}{10}$	$n = 1\frac{1}{4}$	$n = \frac{9}{10}$	$n = 1\frac{3}{16}$

If you have more time

Draw a picture like one of these. Ask your partner to make up a real-world problem that matches your picture.

Get Started or

Get 10 squares in one color and 10 in another color.
Get two number cubes. Take turns with another player or team.
Talk about math as you play!

At Your Turn

Toss two number cubes. Add the dots. Find your toss below.
Follow the directions. Explain your thinking. Cover the answer.
If the answer is taken, lose your turn. Have fun!

Toss	Find the corresponding fraction for each division problem. Explain.
2	7 ÷ 30
3	1 ÷ 3
4	5 ÷ 16
5	8 ÷ 27
6	4 ÷ 15
7	11 ÷ 12
8	8 ÷ 9
9	29 ÷ 30
10	2 ÷ 7
11	17 ÷ 18
12	5 ÷ 8

$\frac{29}{30}$	$\frac{8}{27}$	$\frac{8}{9}$	$\frac{1}{3}$
$\frac{11}{12}$	$\frac{5}{16}$	$\frac{2}{7}$	$\frac{4}{15}$
$\frac{17}{18}$	$\frac{4}{15}$	$\frac{7}{30}$	$\frac{8}{9}$
$\frac{8}{27}$	$\frac{29}{30}$	$\frac{5}{8}$	$\frac{11}{12}$

How to Win

You win if you are the first to get four connected rectangles, like:

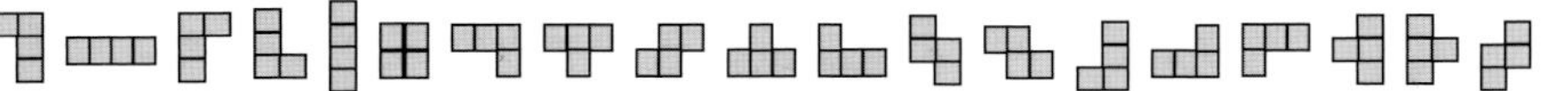

If you have more time Play again!

Get 10 squares in one color and 10 in another color.
Get two number cubes. Take turns with another player or team.
Talk about math as you play!

At Your Turn

Toss two number cubes. Add the dots. Find your toss below.
Follow the directions. Explain your thinking. Cover the answer.
If the answer is taken, lose your turn. Have fun!

Toss	Find the corresponding fraction in simplest form for each division problem. Explain.
2	3 ÷ 9
3	4 ÷ 24
4	10 ÷ 25
5	8 ÷ 28
6	9 ÷ 30
7	16 ÷ 24
8	56 ÷ 64
9	45 ÷ 54
10	36 ÷ 72
11	18 ÷ 24
12	8 ÷ 14

$\frac{7}{8}$	$\frac{2}{7}$	$\frac{3}{10}$	$\frac{1}{3}$
$\frac{3}{4}$	$\frac{4}{7}$	$\frac{2}{3}$	$\frac{5}{6}$
$\frac{3}{10}$	$\frac{1}{6}$	$\frac{7}{8}$	$\frac{2}{7}$
$\frac{2}{3}$	$\frac{1}{2}$	$\frac{5}{6}$	$\frac{2}{5}$

How to Win

You win if you are the first to get four connected rectangles, like:

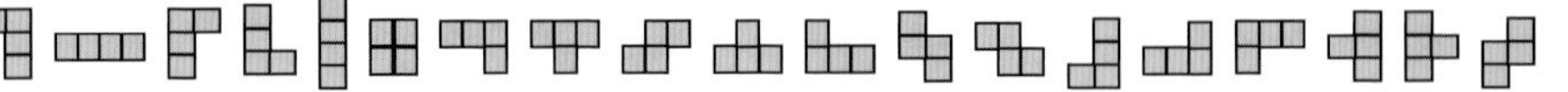

Play again!

Get Started or

Get 10 squares in one color and 10 in another color. Get two number cubes. Take turns with another player or team. Talk about math as you play!

At Your Turn

Toss two number cubes. Add the dots. Find your toss below. Follow the directions. Explain your thinking. Cover the answer. If the answer is taken, lose your turn. Have fun!

Toss	Read the multiplication expression. Explain how to find the product.
2	$\frac{1}{4}$ of 20
3	$\frac{1}{7}$ of 42
4	$\frac{1}{5} \times 40$
5	$\frac{2}{3} \times 27$
6	$80 \times \frac{4}{5}$
7	$(\frac{1}{2} - \frac{1}{4}) \times 44$
8	$64 \times \frac{7}{8}$
9	$\frac{7}{8}$ of 88
10	$\frac{1}{9}$ of 90
11	$\frac{1}{2}$ of 60
12	$\frac{1}{3}$ of 45

6	64	30	8
15	18	56	64
77	10	11	5
11	56	77	18

How to Win

You win if you are the first to get four connected rectangles, like:

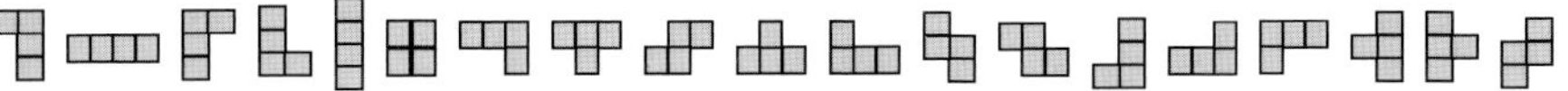

If you have more time

Play again!

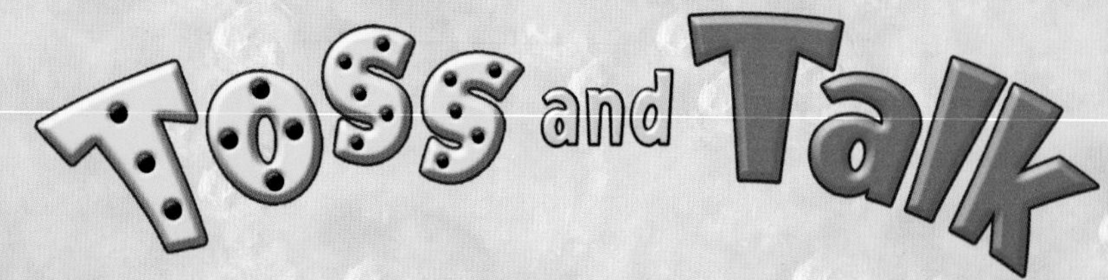

Get Started Get 10 squares in one color and 10 in another color. Get two number cubes. Take turns with another player or team. Talk about math as you play!

At Your Turn Toss two number cubes. Add the dots. Find your toss below. Follow the directions. Explain your thinking. Cover the answer. If the answer is taken, lose your turn. Have fun!

Toss	Read the product. Find the factors you can multiply to get that product.
2	The product is 21.
3	The product is 15.
4	The product is 22.
5	The product is 12.
6	The product is 72.
7	The product is 27.
8	The product is 26.
9	The product is 20.
10	The product is 5.
11	The product is 35.
12	The product is 11.

$\frac{2}{5}$ of 30	$110 \times \frac{1}{5}$	$\frac{2}{3}$ of 39	$\frac{1}{2} \times 70$
$\frac{1}{9} \times 45$	$25 \times \frac{8}{10}$	$\frac{9}{10}$ of 80	$(\frac{2}{3} - \frac{1}{2}) \times 162$
$\frac{8}{9}$ of 81	$90 \times \frac{1}{6}$	$\frac{1}{4}$ of 84	$\frac{1}{3}$ of 33
$\frac{3}{4}$ of 36	$\frac{1}{5}$ of 60	$\frac{2}{5}$ of 65	$\frac{2}{3} \times 30$

How to Win You win if you are the first to get four connected rectangles, like:

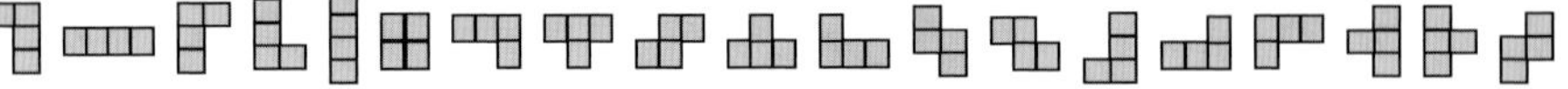

Play again!

Get Started or — Get 10 squares in one color and 10 in another color, two paper clips, and two number cubes. Take turns.

At Your Turn — Toss two cubes to find your ovals. **EXAMPLE:** Choose the 3rd oval on the left and the 5th oval on the right, **or** choose the 5th oval on the left and the 3rd oval on the right. Mark your ovals with paper clips.

How to Play — Round the fraction in each oval to the nearest whole number. Explain how to estimate the product of those numbers. Cover the factors that help you to make an estimate. Lose your turn if the answer is taken.

How to Win — The first player or team to get any three connected rectangles in a row or column wins.

Left ovals					Right ovals
$1\frac{7}{8}$	5 x 9	4 x 9	7 x 9	2 x 3	$8\frac{5}{6}$
$5\frac{3}{7}$	4 x 3	7 x 8	7 x 3	4 x 8	$6\frac{4}{9}$
$3\frac{3}{4}$	5 x 6	2 x 9	7 x 6	5 x 8	$7\frac{2}{3}$
$7\frac{2}{5}$	2 x 8	5 x 3	4 x 6	2 x 6	$2\frac{1}{2}$
$5\frac{3}{7}$					$7\frac{2}{3}$
$3\frac{3}{4}$					$6\frac{4}{9}$

If you have more time — Play again! Talk about how you know whether a fraction is greater than $\frac{1}{2}$, or less than $\frac{1}{2}$.

Get Started Get 10 squares in one color and 10 in another color, one paper clip, paper and a pencil, and one number cube. Take turns.

At Your Turn Toss one cube to find your oval. **EXAMPLE:** [3] Choose the 3rd oval on the left, **or** choose the 3rd oval on the right. Mark your oval with a paper clip.

How to Play Use compatible numbers to estimate the product of the numbers in the oval you chose. Explain your thinking. Cover the answer. Lose your turn if the answer is taken.

How to Win The first player or team to get any three connected rectangles in a row or column wins.

Left ovals:

1. $\frac{3}{2} \times 19\frac{1}{3}$
2. $9\frac{2}{3} \times 1\frac{2}{5}$
3. $\frac{7}{9} \times 46\frac{1}{2}$
4. $\frac{2}{3} \times 23\frac{5}{8}$
5. $\frac{4}{5} \times 23\frac{5}{8}$
6. $2\frac{1}{5} \times 19\frac{1}{8}$

8	20	40	25
35	6	30	16
9	40	35	15
14	12	20	16

Right ovals:

1. $\frac{3}{8} \times 30\frac{1}{2}$
2. $\frac{5}{6} \times 17\frac{1}{3}$
3. $\frac{3}{7} \times 12\frac{2}{3}$
4. $1\frac{1}{2} \times 6\frac{1}{5}$
5. $1\frac{2}{3} \times 14\frac{4}{5}$
6. $\frac{4}{9} \times 19\frac{1}{3}$

Play again! Talk about your strategies as you play.

Get 10 squares in one color and 10 in another color, two paper clips, and two number cubes. Take turns.

At Your Turn

Toss two cubes to find your ovals. **EXAMPLE:** [3] [5] Choose the 3rd oval on the left and the 5th oval on the right, **or** choose the 5th oval on the left and the 3rd oval on the right. Mark your ovals with paper clips.

How to Play

Explain how to multiply the two fractions you chose. Say an equation that includes the product. Find and cover the product. Lose your turn if the answer is taken.

How to Win

The first player or team to get any three connected rectangles in a row or column wins.

Left ovals: $\frac{1}{2}$, $\frac{2}{5}$, $\frac{3}{7}$, $\frac{9}{10}$, $\frac{1}{2}$, $\frac{2}{5}$

$\frac{1}{6}$	$\frac{3}{28}$	$\frac{1}{10}$	$\frac{3}{7}$
$\frac{8}{45}$	$\frac{4}{21}$	$\frac{9}{40}$	$\frac{1}{7}$
$\frac{2}{9}$	$\frac{2}{5}$	$\frac{1}{8}$	$\frac{3}{10}$
$\frac{12}{35}$	$\frac{18}{49}$	$\frac{2}{15}$	$\frac{27}{35}$

Right ovals: $\frac{1}{3}$, $\frac{1}{4}$, $\frac{4}{9}$, $\frac{6}{7}$, $\frac{1}{4}$, $\frac{4}{9}$

Play again! Explain your steps aloud as you multiply. Tell why the answer is less than 1.

Get 10 squares in one color and 10 in another color, one paper clip, and one number cube. Take turns.

At Your Turn Toss one cube to find your oval. **EXAMPLE:** Choose the 3rd oval on the left **or** choose the the 3rd oval on the right. Mark your oval with a paper clip.

How to Play The number you chose is a product. Find the expression that you can compute to get that product. Explain your choice. Cover the answer. Lose your turn if the answer is taken.

How to Win The first player or team to get any three connected rectangles in a row or column wins.

Left ovals: $\frac{5}{11}$, $\frac{4}{15}$, $\frac{3}{5}$, $\frac{2}{3}$, $\frac{7}{20}$, $\frac{6}{35}$

$\frac{1}{2} \times \frac{6}{11}$	$\frac{3}{7} \times \frac{2}{5}$	$\frac{5}{11} \times \frac{3}{5}$	$\frac{7}{8} \times \frac{24}{35}$
$\frac{2}{3} \times \frac{3}{7}$	$\frac{2}{7} \times \frac{1}{2}$	$\frac{9}{10} \times \frac{7}{18}$	$\frac{5}{6} \times \frac{1}{2}$
$\frac{10}{11} \times \frac{1}{2}$	$\frac{1}{2} \times \frac{1}{2}$	$\frac{4}{9} \times \frac{3}{5}$	$\frac{4}{5} \times \frac{20}{24}$
$\frac{3}{4} \times \frac{4}{12}$	$\frac{1}{2} \times \frac{7}{10}$	$\frac{2}{3} \times \frac{5}{7}$	$\frac{1}{2} \times \frac{4}{7}$

Right ovals: $\frac{10}{21}$, $\frac{5}{12}$, $\frac{2}{7}$, $\frac{3}{11}$, $\frac{1}{7}$, $\frac{1}{4}$

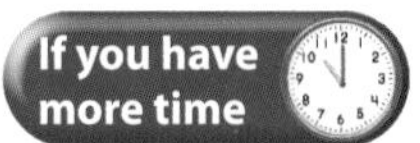

Play again! Talk about your strategies as you play.

Teamwork

Put 1 2 3 4 in a bag.

Choose **a, b, c, d, e,** or **f**.
Pick a tile. Pick two tiles if your group has only two students.
Do the jobs listed below in order.
To find your job, find the number that matches the tile you chose.

 **Decide which formula to use. Choose $A = s \times s$ or $A = l \times w$.**

 **Replace each variable in the formula with a number.**

 **Determine the area of the shape in square units.**

 **Does the answer make sense? How do you know? Explain.**

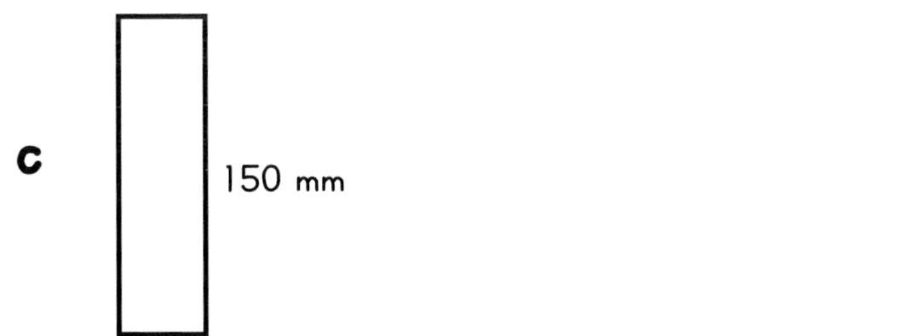

a

b 15 ft

c 150 mm, 20 mm

d 30 yd

e 22 m

f 21 m, 9 m

Create rectangles with other dimensions.
Follow steps 1 – 4 for your shapes.

Teamwork

Put 1 2 3 4 in a bag.

Repeat for Each Round

Choose **a**, **b**, **c**, **d**, **e**, or **f**.
Pick a tile. Pick two tiles if your group has only two students.
Do the jobs listed below in order.
To find your job, find the number that matches the tile you chose.

 **Identify a strategy for finding the missing side lengths.**

 **Determine the missing side length.**

 **Discuss whether or not other strategies are possible.**

 **Does the answer make sense? How do you know? Explain.**

a 9 m
Area = 135 square meters

b 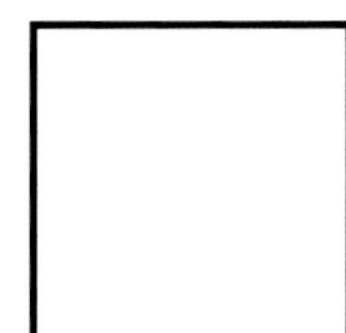
Area = 100 square feet

c 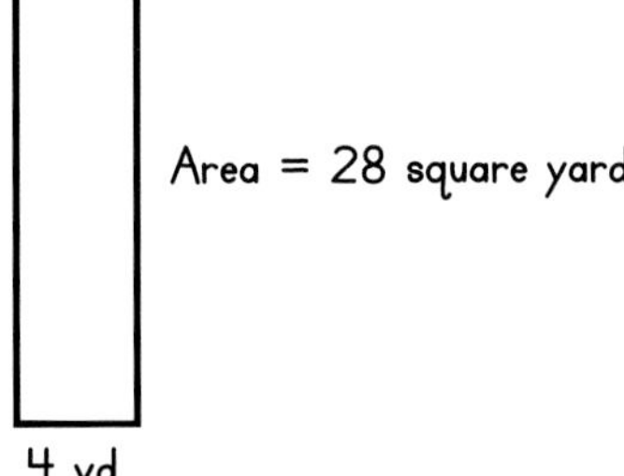
Area = 28 square yards
4 yd

d 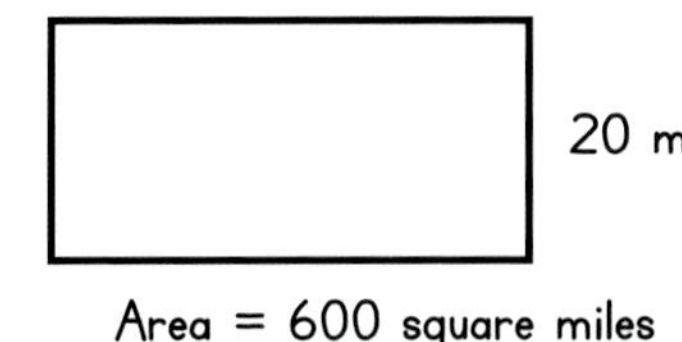
20 mi
Area = 600 square miles

e Area = 144 square meters

f 16 ft
Area = 320 square feet

Create your own area problems like these. Follow steps 1 – 4.

Teamwork

Get paper and a pencil.
Put 1 2 3 4 in a bag.

Repeat for Each Round

Choose **a, b, c, d, e,** or **f**.
Pick a tile. Pick two tiles if your group has only two students.
Do the jobs listed below in order.
To find your job, find the number that matches the tile you chose.

 **Read the two factors aloud to your team.**

 **Explain how to estimate the product of the two factors.**

 **Work with your team to find the exact product. Check the answer.**

 **Compare the exact product from step 3 with the estimate from step 2. Decide if the answer is reasonable.**

a	$5\frac{1}{2} \times 3\frac{1}{5}$	**b**	$4\frac{1}{3} \times 2\frac{3}{4}$
c	$1\frac{1}{3} \times 6\frac{1}{3}$	**d**	$\frac{7}{8} \times 9\frac{1}{3}$
e	$2\frac{4}{5} \times 3\frac{1}{7}$	**f**	$2\frac{1}{2} \times 2\frac{1}{2}$

As a team, choose two mixed numbers.
Work together to multiply those mixed numbers.

Teamwork

Get paper and a pencil.
Put 1 2 3 4 in a bag.

Repeat for Each Round

Choose **a**, **b**, **c**, or **d**.
Pick a tile. Pick two tiles if your group has only two students.
Do the jobs listed below in order.
To find your job, find the number that matches the tile you chose.

 **Read the question aloud. Tell your team which information from the chart you will need to answer the question.**

 **Work with your team to answer the question. Check the answer.**

 **Create a new question by changing the day of the week in the problem.**

 **Work with your team to answer the question created in step 3. Check the answer.**

Hours Gary Worked Last Week

Day	Hours Worked
Monday	$4\frac{2}{3}$
Tuesday	$8\frac{1}{3}$
Wednesday	$5\frac{1}{4}$
Thursday	$6\frac{2}{3}$

a. Gary worked twice as many hours this Thursday as last Thursday. How many hours did he work this Thursday?

b. This Tuesday, Gary worked $1\frac{1}{2}$ times as many hours as he did last Tuesday. How many hours did he work this Tuesday?

c. This Wednesday, Gary worked $1\frac{1}{5}$ times as many hours as he did last Tuesday. How many hours did he work this Wednesday?

d. This Monday, Gary worked only $\frac{1}{2}$ the time he worked last Monday. How many hours did he work this Monday?

Create another question that your team can answer using the data in the chart.

Quick Questions

Each player tosses two number cubes.
If your numbers match another player's numbers, toss again.
Decide who will read the first question. Take turns.

For Each Question

Listen to the reader. Discuss and agree on the correct answer.
Every player who has that answer can remove one cube that shows the answer.

How to Win

The first player who removes both cubes wins. Have fun!

a	What is the missing digit in this factor pair for 45? ☐, 15
b	What is the missing digit in this factor pair for 38? ☐, 19
c	What is the missing digit in this factor pair for 40? ☐, 8
d	What is the missing digit in this factor pair for 75? ☐, 75
e	What is the missing digit in this factor pair for 48? ☐, 12
f	What is the missing digit in this factor pair for 54? ☐, 9
g	What is the missing digit in this factor pair for 55? 5, 1☐
h	What is the missing digit in this factor pair for 90? ☐, 18
i	What is the missing digit in this factor pair for 96? 8, 1☐
j	What is the missing digit in this factor pair for 81? ☐, 27
k	What is the missing digit in this factor pair for 84? 4, 2☐
l	What is the missing digit in this factor pair for 96? 3, 3☐
m	What is the missing digit in this factor pair for 21? ☐, 7

n	What is the missing digit in this factor pair for 36? ☐, 9
o	What is the missing digit in this factor pair for 30? 2, 1☐
p	What is the missing digit in this factor pair for 18? ☐, 6
q	What is the missing digit in this factor pair for 24? ☐, 12
r	What is the missing digit in this factor pair for 60? 4, ☐5
s	What is the missing digit in this factor pair for 75? 3, 2☐
t	What is the missing digit in this factor pair for 32? ☐, 8
u	What is the missing digit in this factor pair for 51? ☐, 17
v	What is the missing digit in this factor pair for 77? 7, 1☐
w	What is the missing digit in this factor pair for 84? 2. 4☐
x	What is the missing digit in this factor pair for 65? ☐, 13
y	What is the missing digit in this factor pair for 27? ☐, 9
z	What is the missing digit in this factor pair for 72? 3, 2☐

Toss two number cubes again. Play another game.
Begin with the next question in the list.

Quick Questions

Each player tosses two number cubes.
If your numbers match another player's numbers, toss again.
Decide who will read the first question. Take turns.

For Each Question

Listen to the reader. Discuss and agree on the correct answer.
Every player who has that answer can remove one cube that shows the number in front of that answer.

How to Win

The first player who removes both cubes wins. Have fun!

a	Which one of these is a factor pair of 110? **1)** 2, 55 **2)** 5, 21 **3)** 4, 28	n	Which one of these is not a factor pair of 62? **4)** 2, 31 **5)** 1, 62 **6)** 3, 24
b	Which one of these is not a factor pair of 84? **4)** 7, 12 **5)** 8, 12 **6)** 6, 14	o	Which one of these is a factor pair of 56? **1)** 4, 14 **2)** 3, 18 **3)** 7, 9
c	Which one of these is a factor pair of 85? **1)** 3, 25 **2)** 5, 15 **3)** 5, 17	p	Which one of these is not a factor pair of 84? **4)** 7, 12 **5)** 6, 19 **6)** 4, 21
d	Which one of these is not a factor pair of 82? **4)** 4, 21 **5)** 2, 41 **6)** 1, 82	q	Which one of these is a factor pair of 96? **1)** 3, 24 **2)** 8, 12 **3)** 4, 22
e	Which one of these is a factor pair of 34? **1)** 4, 9 **2)** 2, 17 **3)** 3, 11	r	Which one of these is not a factor pair of 75? **4)** 6, 15 **5)** 3, 25 **6)** 5, 15
f	Which one of these is not a factor pair of 102? **4)** 2, 51 **5)** 6, 17 **6)** 8, 15	s	Which one of these is a factor pair of 27? **1)** 4, 6 **2)** 3, 9 **3)** 6, 7
g	Which one of these is not a factor pair of 72? **1)** 9, 8 **2)** 4, 36 **3)** 3, 24	t	Which one of these is not a factor pair of 78? **4)** 6, 13 **5)** 4, 17 **6)** 2, 39
h	Which one of these is a factor pair of 76? **4)** 4, 19 **5)** 3, 26 **6)** 6, 12	u	Which one of these is a factor pair of 92? **1)** 4, 23 **2)** 3, 34 **3)** 7, 12
i	Which one of these is a factor pair of 106? **1)** 4, 24 **2)** 8, 14 **3)** 2, 53	v	Which one of these is a factor pair of 105? **4)** 3, 35 **5)** 2, 52 **6)** 8, 15
j	Which one of these is a factor pair of 108? **4)** 8, 14 **5)** 3, 36 **6)** 7, 16	w	Which one of these is not a factor pair of 112? **1)** 4, 28 **2)** 8, 14 **3)** 8, 16
k	Which one of these is not a factor pair of 68? **1)** 3, 32 **2)** 4, 17 **3)** 2, 34	x	Which one of these is a factor pair of 88? **4)** 8, 12 **5)** 6, 14 **6)** 4, 22
l	Which one of these is a factor pair of 94? **4)** 3, 28 **5)** 4, 26 **6)** 2, 47	y	Which one of these is not a factor pair of 32? **1)** 4, 16 **2)** 2, 16 **3)** 4, 8
m	Which one of these is a factor pair of 100? **1)** 4, 20 **2)** 5, 25 **3)** 4, 25	z	Which one of these is a factor pair of 54? **4)** 6, 8 **5)** 3, 18 **6)** 4, 9

Play another game. Begin with the next question in the list.
Or make up your own questions like these.

Teamwork

Get Started 

Put 1 2 3 4 in a bag.

Repeat for Each Round

Let each team member choose and read one or two facts until every fact is read aloud. Ask one team member to pick a tile and to read the problem next to that tile number. Determine which fact answers a hidden question in that problem. Work as a team to solve the problem. Use the tile to cover the correct answer.

a. The total cost of the tickets is $128.00.

b. The mileage charge is $6.00.

c. $53.50 can be spent for the socks.

d. The average rate is 4.5 minutes per kilometer.

1 Martin goes to the theatre in a taxi. The taxi costs $4 plus a mileage charge of 50¢ for every half-mile. It is 6 miles to the theatre. What is the cost of the taxi ride in dollars?

2 Teri finished a 5 kilometer run in 22.5 minutes. Mark ran at the same rate but for 8 kilometers. For how many minutes did Mark run?

3 Tajah had $150. She bought 4 circus tickets at $32 each. How many dollars does she have left?

4 Carmen wants to buy sports socks for her team. They cost $3.50 per pair. She has $55 but must have $1.50 left to get home on the bus. How many pairs of socks can she buy?

15	22	36	10

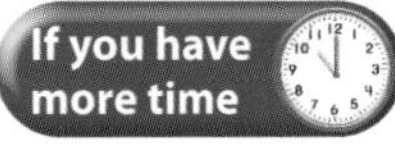

Write a problem that has a hidden question.
Ask a partner to solve your problem.

Teamwork

Get Started or

Put 1 2 3 in a bag.

Repeat for Each Round

Pick a tile. Read aloud the question next to that number.
Find problem **a**, **b**, or **c** for which your question is a hidden question.
Find the other hidden question needed to solve that problem.
Work with your team to answer both questions and to solve the problem.
Use your tile to cover the answer at the bottom of the page.

	The First Hidden Question	The Other Hidden Question
1	**How much did she make on commission?**	**What is the area of the rectangle?**
2	**How much did he spend in all?**	**How much did he spend for CDs?**
3	**What is the area of the triangle? (The area of a triangle is $\frac{1}{2}$ base times altitude.)**	**What is the difference between her total salary and her commission?**

a

The length of a rectangle is 10 cm and the width is 6 cm. A triangle has a base of 10 cm and an altitude of 8 cm. What is the difference in square centimeters between the area of the rectangle and the area of the triangle?

b

Logan had $83 to spend. He bought 8 CDs at $6.50 each and spent $6 for his lunch. How many dollars does Logan have left?

c

Madison makes $7 an hour at the jewelry store. She also gets a 10% commission on whatever she sells. Last week she sold $1,500 worth of jewelry. Her total pay for the week was $360. How many hours did she work last week?

25	30	20

If you have more time

Choose **a**, **b**, or **c**. Change the numbers in the problem.
Ask your partner to solve the problem with your numbers.

Read a question. Explain how to use a diagram to answer the question. Display each 0 – 9 tile exactly once. If you have a partner, take turns.

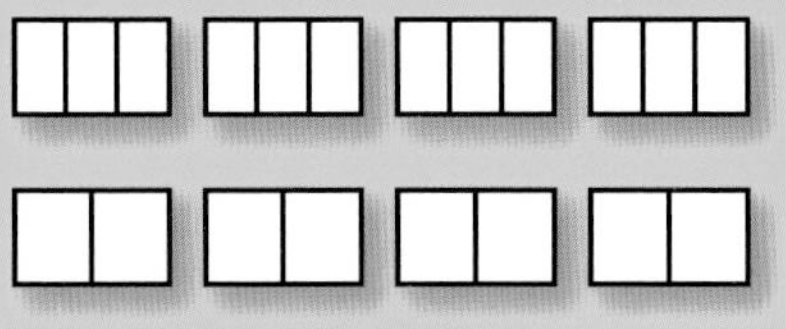

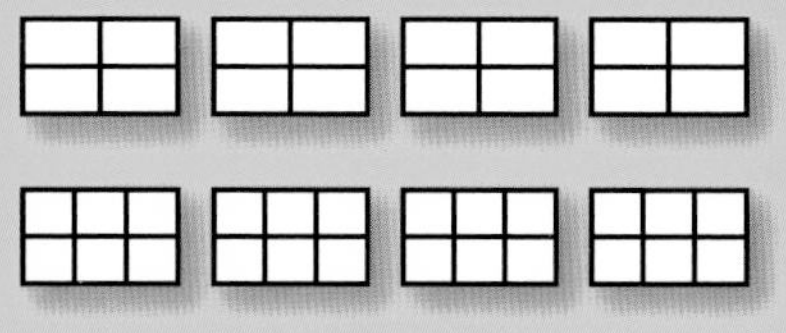

a. How many thirds are in 2?

b. How many fourths are in $1\frac{3}{4}$?

c. How many fourths are in 2?

d. How many two-thirds are in $1\frac{1}{3}$?

e. How many halves are in 0?

f. How many halves are in $2\frac{1}{2}$?

g. How many sixths are in $1\frac{1}{2}$?

h. How many three-fourths are in 3?

i. How many sixths are in $\frac{1}{6}$?

j. How many five-sixths are in $2\frac{1}{2}$?

Use the diagrams to make up other questions about division. Ask your partner to display the answers with 0 – 9 tiles.

Display the Digits

0 1 2 3 4 5 6 7 8 9

Pick a tile. Find the question next to that number. Point to the expression you can evaluate to answer the question. Explain how to find the answer. Use your tile to cover the answer at the bottom of the page. Display each 0 – 9 tile exactly once. If you have a partner, take turns.

0 How many fourths are in $3\frac{1}{4}$?

1 How many thirds are in 4?

2 How many halves are in $3\frac{1}{2}$?

3 How many eighths are in 4?

4 How many sixths are in $2\frac{1}{3}$?

5 How many two-thirds are in $2\frac{2}{3}$?

6 How many three-fourths are in 6?

7 How many three-fourths are in 12?

8 How many halves are in $2\frac{1}{2}$?

9 How many five-sixths are in 5?

$3\frac{1}{2} \div \frac{1}{2}$ $2\frac{2}{3} \times \frac{3}{2}$

$2\frac{1}{2} \times 2$ $4 \div \frac{1}{3}$

$2\frac{1}{3} \div \frac{1}{6}$ $12 \times \frac{4}{3}$

$3\frac{1}{4} \div \frac{1}{4}$ $4 \div \frac{1}{8}$

$6 \times \frac{4}{3}$ $5 \times \frac{6}{5}$

14	32	7	5	16
13	8	12	6	4

Make up a question like one of these so your partner can display the answer with a 0 – 9 tile.

Get 10 squares in one color and 10 in another color. Get two number cubes. Take turns with another player or team. Talk about math as you play!

At Your Turn

Toss two number cubes. Add the dots. Find your toss below. Follow the directions. Explain your thinking. Cover the answer. If the answer is taken, lose your turn. Have fun!

Toss	Get paper and a pencil. Read the expression. Explain how to find the quotient.
2	8.5 ÷ 0.5
3	2.24 ÷ 0.8
4	2.4 ÷ 0.3
5	87.4 ÷ 0.38
6	0.427 ÷ 6.1
7	13.3666 ÷ 6.89
8	98.6 ÷ 2.9
9	0.685 ÷ 2.74
10	6.89 ÷ 1.3
11	2.5 ÷ 0.005
12	2.59 ÷ 0.7

2.8	230	34	500
1.94	3.7	230	5.3
0.07	34	0.25	17
0.25	8	1.94	0.07

You win if you are the first to get four connected rectangles, like:

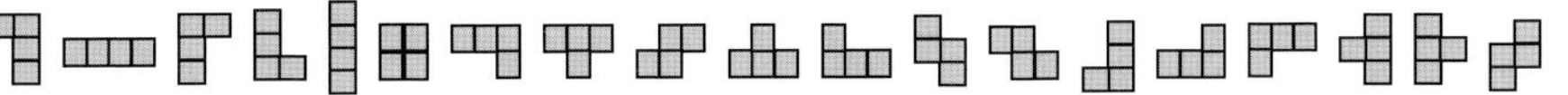

Play again!

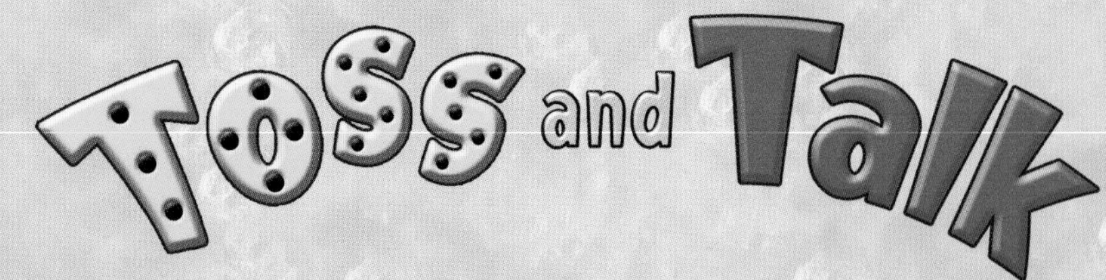

Get 10 squares in one color and 10 in another color. Get two number cubes. Take turns with another player or team. Talk about math as you play!

At Your Turn

Toss two number cubes. Add the dots. Find your toss below. Follow the directions. Explain your thinking. Cover the answer. If the answer is taken, lose your turn. Have fun!

Toss	Get paper and a pencil. This number is the missing digit in a quotient. Find a quotient that has the missing digit.
2	5
3	3
4	1
5	2
6	7
7	0
8	6
9	9
10	1
11	4
12	8

20.24 ÷ 2.2 = ☐.2	52.5 ÷ 4.2 = 1☐.5	0.121 ÷ 1.1 = ☐.11	4.97 ÷ 7.1 = 0.☐
8.82 ÷ 4.2 = 2.☐	2.25 ÷ 1.5 = 1.☐	40.26 ÷ 6.6 = ☐.1	1.43 ÷ 1.1 = ☐.3
64.64 ÷ 80.8 = 0.☐	1.02 ÷ 25.5 = 0.0☐	0.87 ÷ 0.3 = 2.☐	3.63 ÷ 1.1 = 3.☐
24.36 ÷ 1.2 = 2☐.3	0.175 ÷ 2.5 = 0.0☐	12.21 ÷ 5.5 = 2.2☐	2.52 ÷ 4.2 = 0.☐

You win if you are the first to get four connected rectangles, like:

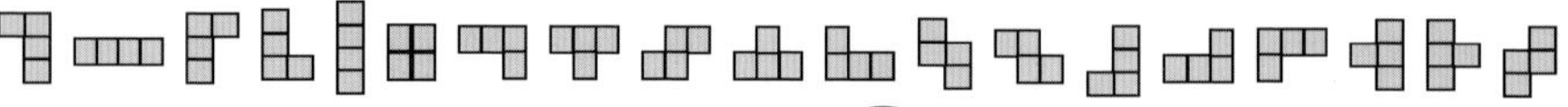

Play again!

Teamwork

Get paper and a pencil.

Put 1 2 3 4 in a bag.

Repeat for Each Round

Choose **a**, **b**, **c**, or **d**.

Pick a tile. Pick two tiles if your group has only two students.

Do the jobs listed below in order.

To find your job, find the number that matches the tile you chose.

 **Read the question aloud. Tell your team members what you know and what you have to find.**

 **Draw and label a picture that will help your team solve the problem.**

 **Write an equation that your team can use to solve the problem.**

 **Work with your team to solve the problem. Check to be sure the answer makes sense.**

a. If one can of corn holds $15\frac{1}{4}$ ounces of corn, how many ounces of corn are in 8 cans?

b. Bob collected $4\frac{2}{3}$ buckets of shells at the beach. Connie collected four times as many buckets. How many buckets of shells did Connie collect?

c. Yasmin cut a piece of yarn $20\frac{3}{4}$ inches long. This is four times as long as Marina's piece of yarn. How long is Marina's piece of yarn?

d. A jar of pasta sauce holds $25\frac{1}{8}$ ounces. How many ounces of pasta sauce are in 3 jars?

Change the numbers in one of the problems.

Work as a team to solve the problem with the new numbers.

Teamwork

Get paper and a pencil.
Put 1 2 3 4 in a bag.

Repeat for Each Round

Choose **a**, **b**, **c**, or **d**.
Pick a tile. Pick two tiles if your group has only two students.
Do the jobs listed below in order.
To find your job, find the number that matches the tile you chose.

 **Read the question aloud. Tell your team members what you know and what you have to find.**

 **Draw a picture and choose an operation. Explain to your team how you made your choice.**

 **Write an equation that will help your team to solve the problem.**

 **Work with your team to solve the problem. Check to be sure the answer makes sense.**

a. Belinda cut a piece of wood $8\frac{1}{3}$ feet long. This is 4 times as long as Sally's piece of wood. How long is Sally's piece of wood?

b. One jar of juice holds 32 ounces. Mike drinks $\frac{1}{3}$ of the jar. How many ounces does he drink?

c. If one bottle of yogurt contains $6\frac{1}{4}$ ounces, how much yogurt is in a 6-pack of yogurt?

d. Wanda volunteered at the zoo for 21 hours last month. This was $3\frac{1}{2}$ times as many hours as Doug volunteered. For how many hours did Doug volunteer?

ZOO

Change the numbers in one of the problems.
Work as a team to solve the problem with the new numbers.

Teamwork

Put 1 2 3 4 in a bag.
Get paper and a pencil.

Repeat for Each Round

Choose **a**, **b**, **c**, or **d**.
Pick a tile. Pick two tiles if your group has only two students.
Do the jobs listed below in order.
To find your job, find the number that matches the tile you chose.

1 **Name the three-dimensional shape.**

2 **Point to each face. Tell your team the number of faces in all.**

3 **Point to each vertex. Tell your team the number of vertices in all.**

4 **Finger trace each edge. Tell your team the number of edges in all.**

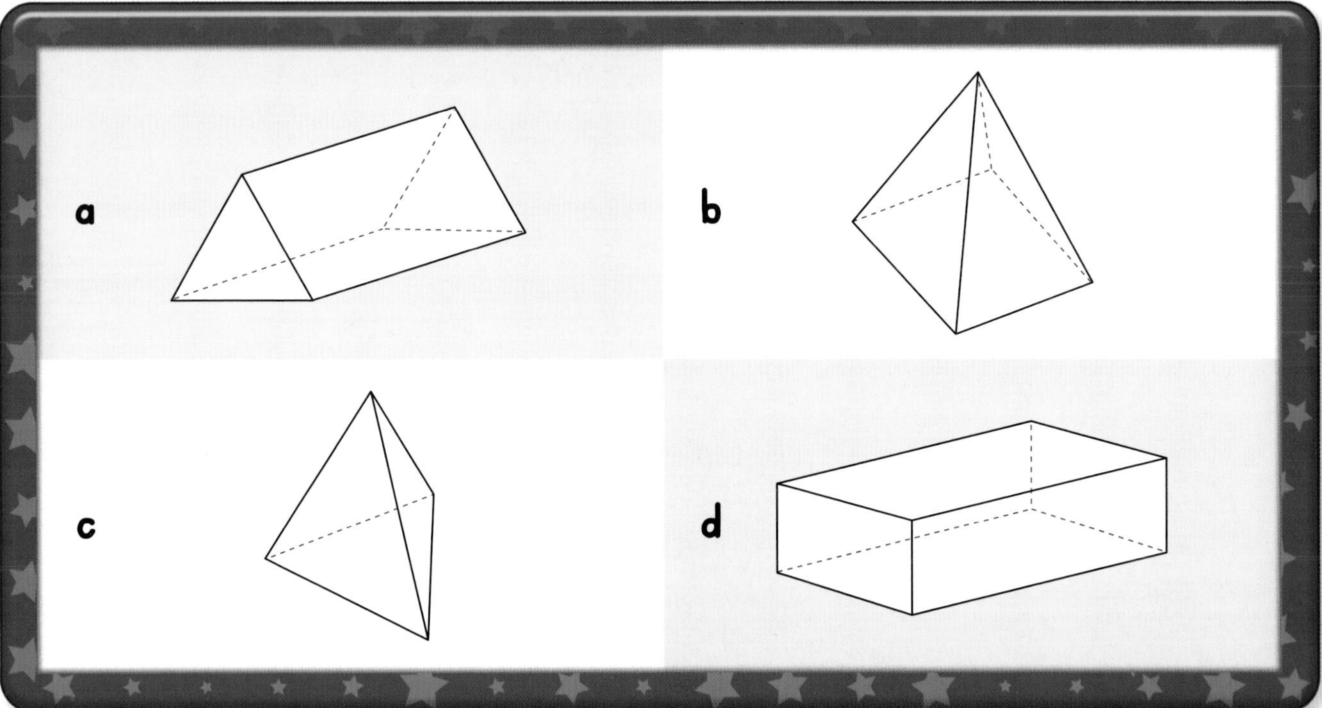

Draw or trace one or more of the three-dimensional shapes.
Use letters to label the vertices.

Center Activity **12-1**

Teamwork

Get Started or

Put 1 2 3 4 in a bag.
Get paper and a pencil.

Repeat for Each Round

Choose **a**, **b**, **c**, or **d**.
Pick a tile. Pick two tiles if your group has only two students.
Do the jobs listed below in order.
To find your job, find the number that matches the tile you chose.

 **Name the three-dimensional shape.**

 **Tell how many faces in all.**

 **Tell how many vertices in all.**

 **Tell how many edges in all.**

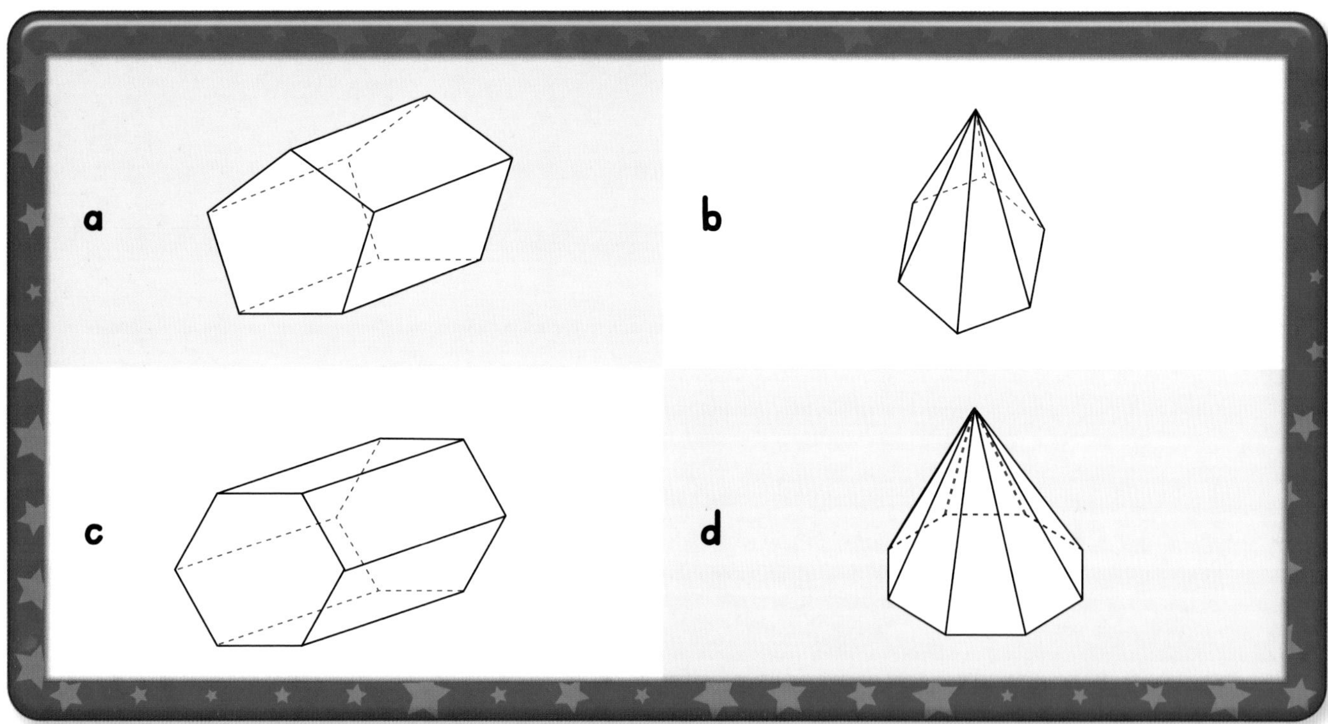

Discuss the relationship between the faces, vertices and edges of three-dimensional shapes. Describe any patterns that you notice.

Teamwork

Get Started

Put 1 2 3 in a bag.
Get paper and a pencil.

Repeat for Each Round

Choose **a**, **b**, **c**, or **d**.
Pick a tile.
Do the jobs listed below in order.
To find your job, find the number that matches the tile you chose.

 **Draw the front view of the cubes.**

 **Draw a side view of the cubes.**

 **Draw a top view of the cubes.**

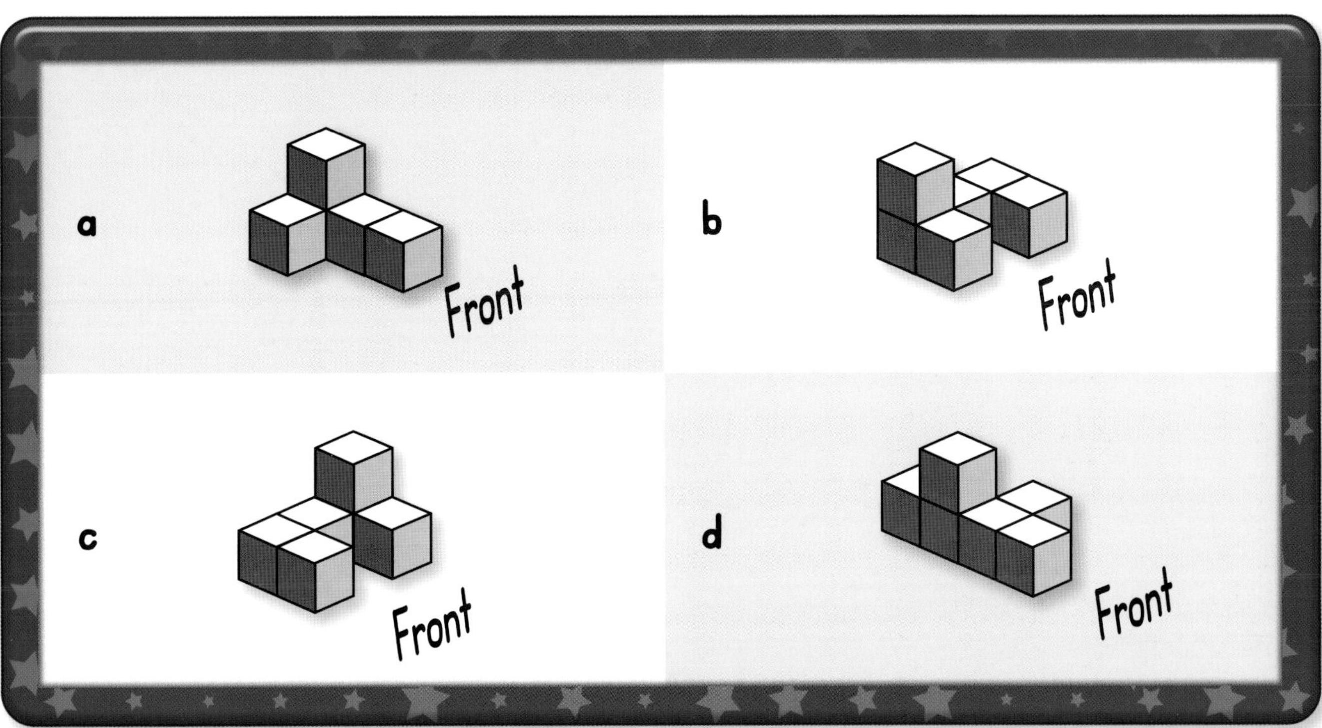

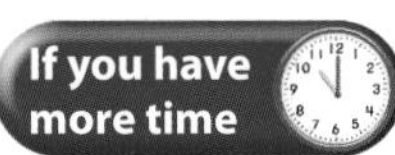

If you have more time

Work together as a team. Use cubes to design other solids.
Discuss and draw the front, side, and top views.

Teamwork

Put 1 2 3 in a bag.
Get paper and a pencil.

Repeat for Each Round

Choose **a, b, c,** or **d.**
Pick a tile.
Do the jobs listed below in order.
To find your job, find the number that matches the tile you chose.

Draw the front view of the cubes.

Draw a side view of the cubes.

Draw a top view of the cubes.

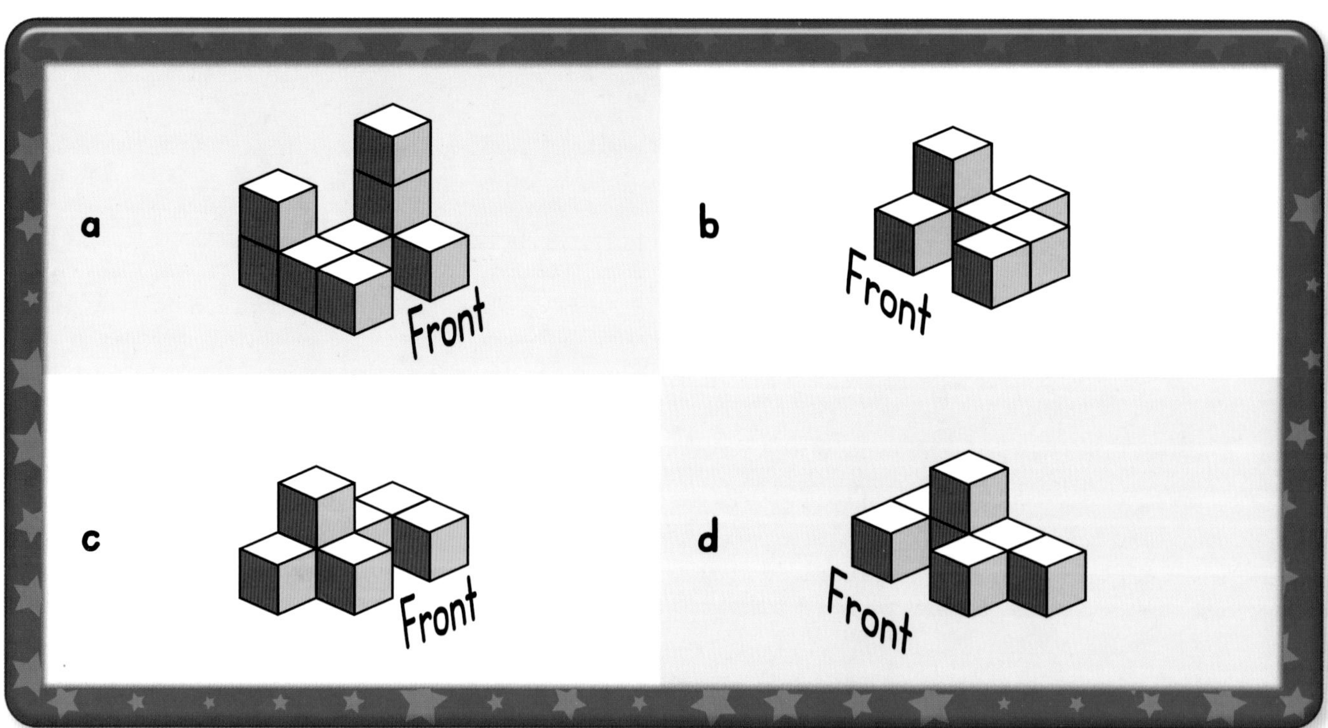

Work together as a team. Use cubes to design other solids.
Discuss and draw the front, side, and top views.

Teamwork

Get Started 

Get 20 squares in one color and 20 in another color.

Repeat for Each Round

Choose **a**, **b**, or **c**. Ask one team member to read the problem and tell the team what is known, and what needs to be found.
Work together. Use your squares to help you solve the problem.

a. Mary wants to tile a floor using red tiles and blue tiles. She wants a red center strip and a surrounding border of single blue tiles. Use your squares to form the pattern. If the center strip has five single red tiles, how many blue tiles does Mary need? If the center strip is two red tiles wide and seven red tiles long, how many blue tiles does Mary need?

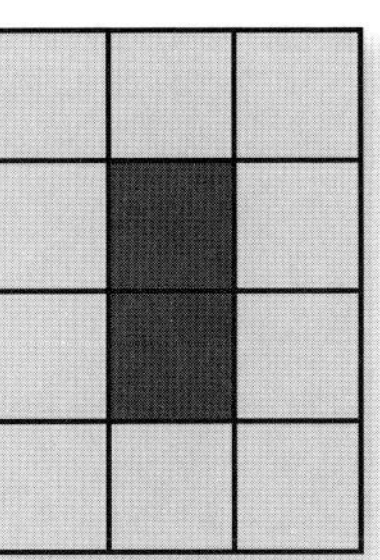

b. John wants to place square red bricks in the center of his patio floor. He wants to surround the square center with a blue border that is one square blue brick wide. Use your squares. Make the pattern, first with only 1 brick in the center, then with 4, then with 9. How many blue bricks will John need if his red square center is 20 bricks long and 20 bricks wide?

c. Form a square checkerboard made up of red and blue squares. If the number of squares along one side is an odd number and the corner square is red, can you always predict the color of the middle square?

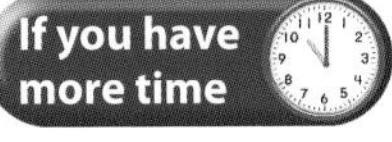

What happens to the middle square in problem **c** if the number of squares along one side of the checkerboard is an even number?

Teamwork

Get 20 squares in one color and 20 in another color.

Repeat for Each Round

Choose **a**, **b**, or **c**. Ask one team member to read the problem and tell the team what is known, and what needs to be found.
Work together. Use your squares to help you solve the problem.

a. How many squares are there in each figure? How many squares would it take to make the tenth figure if the pattern continues?

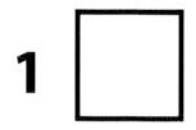

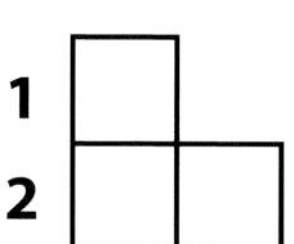

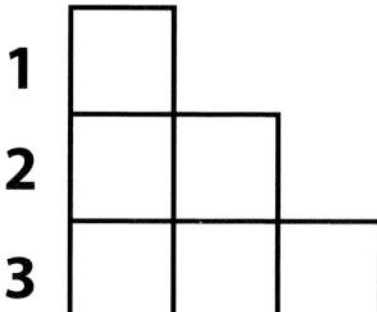

b. If you make the following rectangles with squares, what pattern is suggested for finding the total number of shaded squares? How many shaded squares would there be in the ninth rectangle?

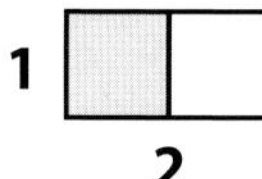

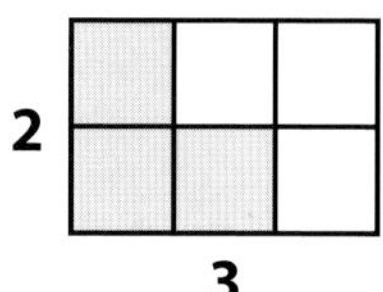

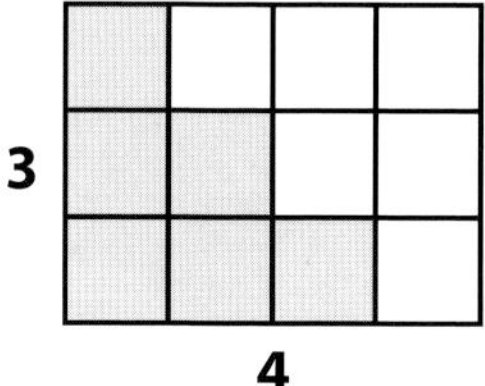

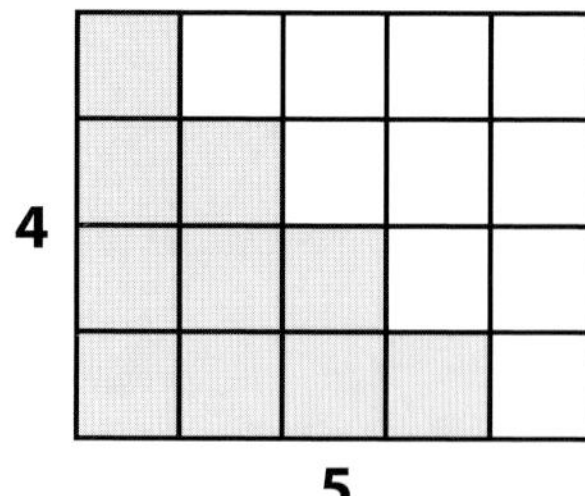

c. If you build steps out of rows of cement blocks that are 4 blocks wide and 1 block high, how many cement blocks will it take to make 10 steps?

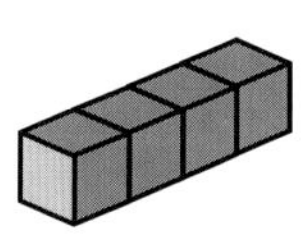
1 Step

2 Steps

3 Steps

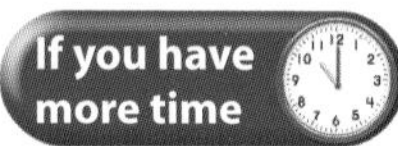

Talk about other ways to solve problem **c**.
Then discuss how all three problems are related.

Teamwork

Center Activity 12-4

Get cubes to build each of the solids.
Put 1 2 3 4 in a bag.

Repeat for Each Round

Choose **a**, **b**, **c**, or **d**.
Pick a tile. Pick two tiles if your group has only two students.
Do the jobs listed below in order.
To find your job, find the number that matches the tile you chose.

Use cubes to make a model of the rectangular prism. Share your model with your team members.

Explain why the model matches the picture. Tell how you know.

Find the volume by counting the number of cubes needed to make the model.

Decide if the answer makes sense. Tell how you know.

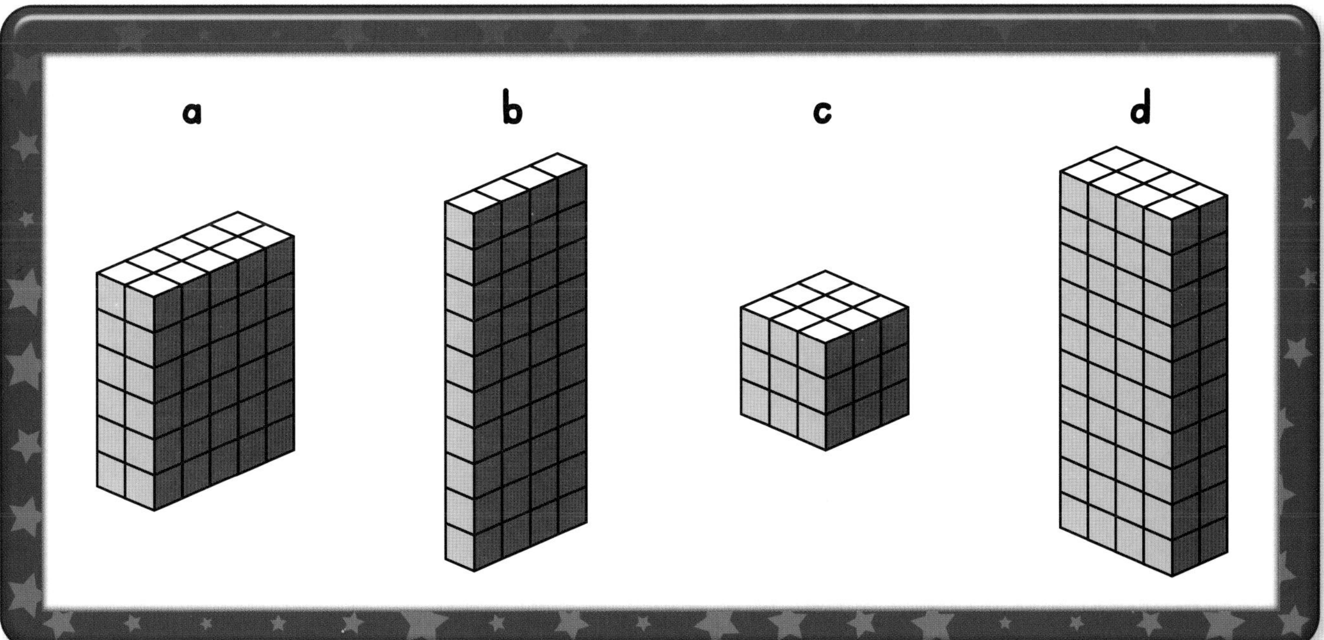

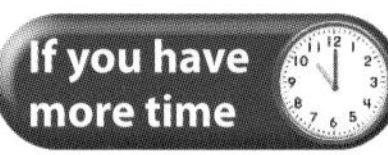

Create other rectangular prisms and cubes.
Find the volume of each of your figures.

Teamwork

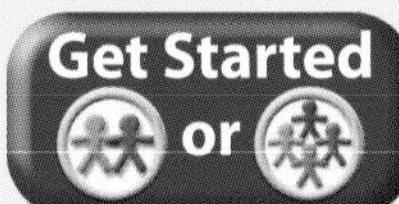

Get cubes to build each of the solids.
Put 1 2 3 4 in a bag.

Repeat for Each Round

Choose **a, b, c,** or **d**.
Pick a tile. Pick two tiles if your group has only two students.
Do the jobs listed below in order.
To find your job, find the number that matches the tile you chose.

Look at the rectangular prism or cube. Decide whether your team should build the solid using cubes, or if you will count the cubes by looking at the drawing.

Using the strategy chosen in Step 1, explain how to find the volume of the rectangular prism or cube.

Create another rectangular prism or cube that has the same volume but different dimensions.

Using the solid figure created in Step 3, explain why two figures with the same volume can have different dimensions.

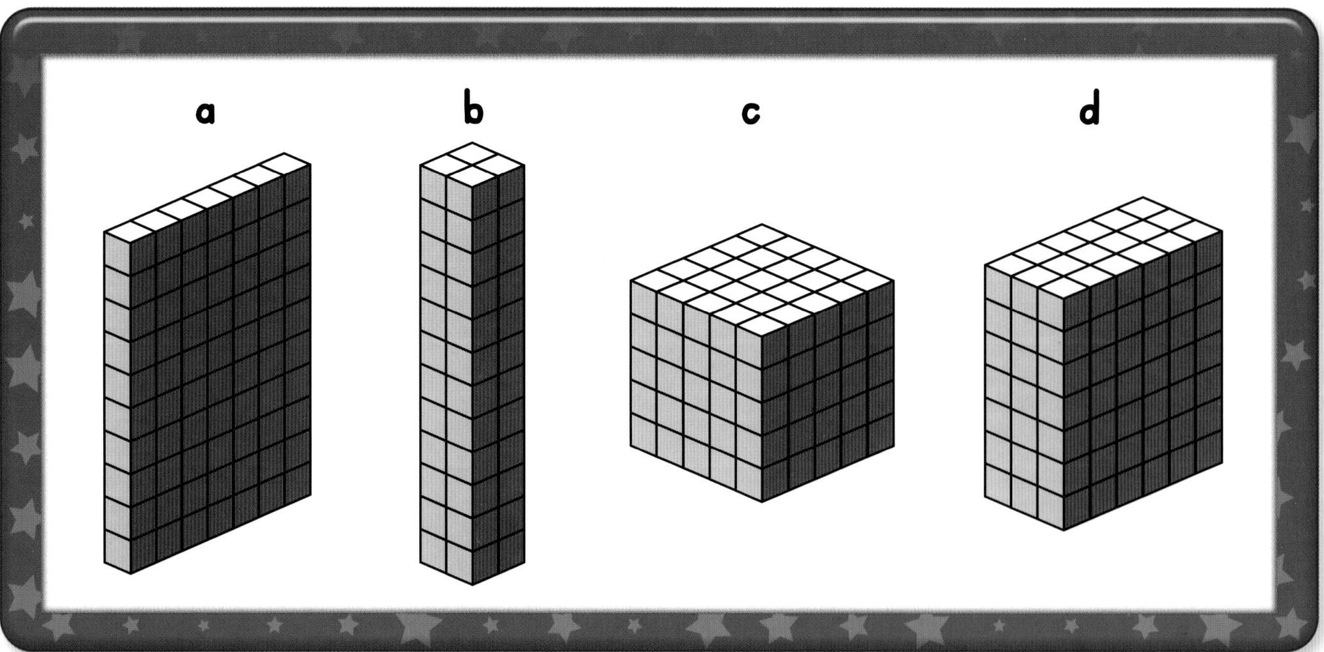

Create two more rectangular prisms that have the same volume but different dimensions.

Get Started or

Get 10 squares in one color and 10 in another color.
Get two number cubes. Take turns with another player or team.
Talk about math as you play!

At Your Turn

Toss two number cubes. Add the dots. Find your toss below.
Follow the directions. Explain your thinking. Cover the answer.
If the answer is taken, lose your turn. Have fun!

Toss	Explain how to find the volume of a rectangular prism with these dimensions. Use paper and pencil if needed.
2	length = 13 feet height = 2 feet width = 5 feet
3	length = 9 yards width = 5 yards height = 4 yards
4	length = 9 meters width = 5 meters height = 7 meters
5	length = 7 centimeters width = 4 centimeters height = 6 centimeters
6	length = 9 inches width = 5 inches height = 11 inches
7	(prism) 18 ft, 12 ft, 13 ft
8	Area of the base: 38 square centimeters Height: 17 centimeters
9	Base area: 47 square meters Height: 16 meters
10	Base area: 59 square inches Height: 6 inches
11	length = 28 feet width = 12 feet height = 10 feet
12	length = 8 feet width = 4 feet height = 7 feet

315 cubic meters	646 cubic centimeters	180 cubic yards	168 cubic centimeters
495 cubic inches	354 cubic inches	2,808 cubic feet	752 cubic meters
224 cubic feet	168 cubic centimeters	3,360 cubic feet	130 cubic feet
2,808 cubic feet	752 cubic meters	495 cubic inches	646 cubic centimeters

How to Win

You win if you are the first to get four connected rectangles, like:

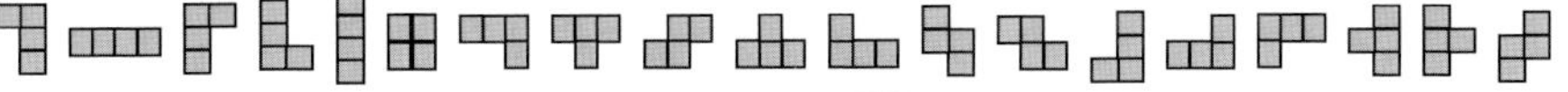

Play again!

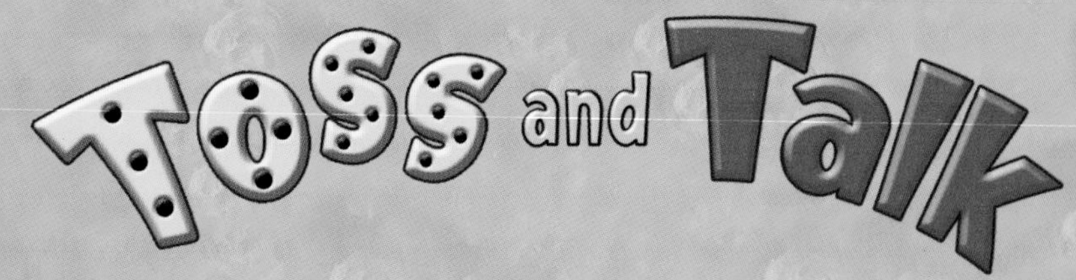

Get 10 squares in one color and 10 in another color.
Get two number cubes. Take turns with another player or team.
Talk about math as you play!

At Your Turn

Toss two number cubes. Add the dots. Find your toss below.
Follow the directions. Explain your thinking. Cover the answer.
If the answer is taken, lose your turn. Have fun!

Toss	Explain how to find the volume or the unknown dimension of the rectangular prism. Use paper and pencil if needed.
2	length = 9 in. width = □ in. height = 10 in. V = 720 cubic inches
3	Volume = 162 cubic centimeters (prism: □ cm, 3 cm, 6 cm)
4	Volume = 336 cubic feet Base area = 48 square feet height = □ ft
5	Volume = □ cubic meters height = 4 m length = 15 m width = 9 m
6	Volume = □ cubic yards height = 12 yd length = 8 yd width = 5 yd
7	Length = 12.5 ft width = 8 ft height = 5.6 ft V = □ cubic feet
8	Volume = 312 cubic centimeters length = 6.5 cm width = □ cm height = 8cm
9	Volume = □ cubic inches length = 32 in. width = 4 in. height = 5 in.
10	length = 10 ft width = 6 ft height = 7 ft Volume = □ cubic feet
11	length = □ m width = 8 m height = 9 m V = 792 cubic meters
12	Volume = 680 cubic yards Base area = 68 square yards height = □ yd

480	640	10	7
6	8	540	420
640	560	6	480
540	11	9	560

How to Win

You win if you are the first to get four connected rectangles, like:

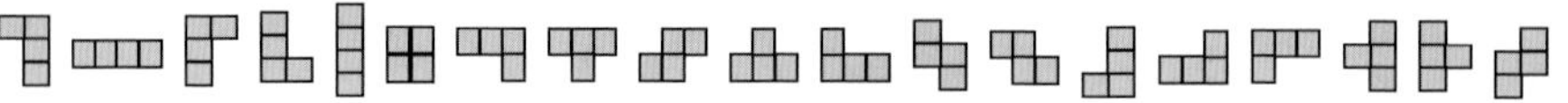

Play again!

Teamwork

Get paper and a pencil.
Put 1 2 3 4 in a bag.

Repeat for Each Round

Choose **a, b, c,** or **d**. Pick two tiles if your group has only two students.
To find your job, find the number that matches the tile you chose.
Do the jobs listed below in order.

1 Work with your team to determine how the solid figure can be divided into two more familiar shapes.

2 Find the volume of one of the familiar shapes.

3 Find the volume of the second familiar shape.

4 Find the total volume of the solid figure.

a

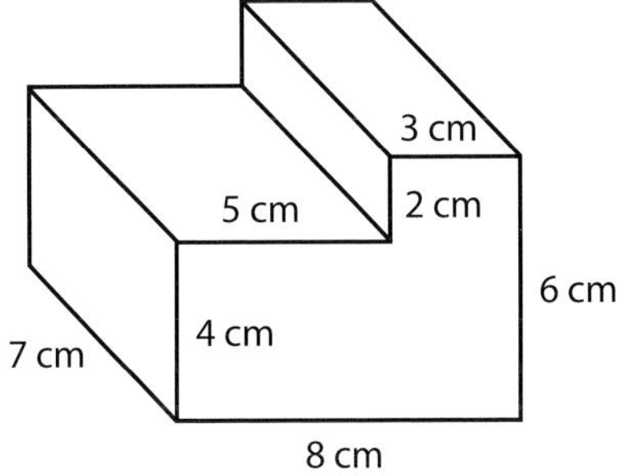

b

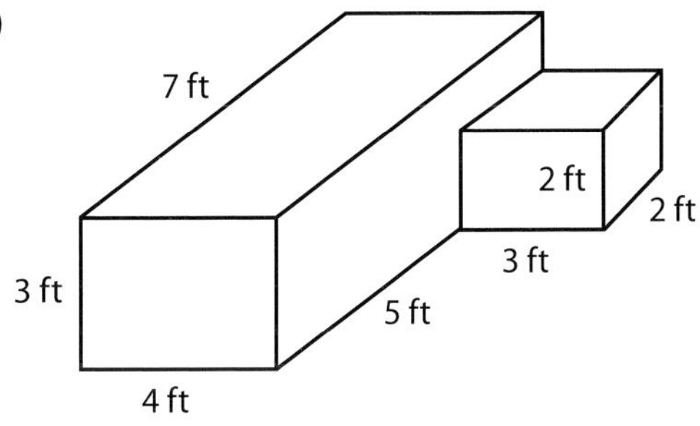

c

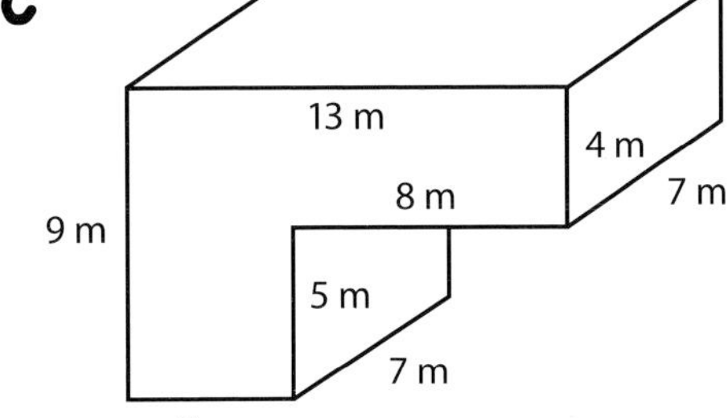

d

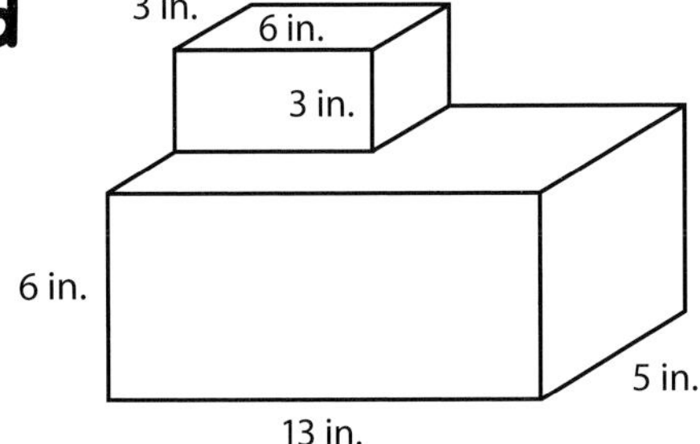

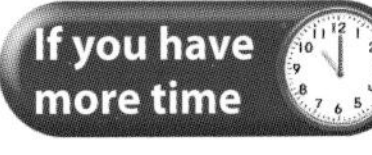

Choose **a** or **c**. Find more than one way to divide the solid figure into two familiar shapes. Calculate the volume of the figure both ways.

Teamwork

Get paper and a pencil.
Put 1 2 3 4 in a bag.

Repeat for Each Round

Choose **a**, **b**, **c**, or **d**. Pick a tile. Pick two tiles if your group has only two students. Do the jobs listed below in order.
To find your job, find the number that matches the tile you chose.

Work with your team to determine where lines can be drawn to divide the given figure into two or more familiar parts.

Work with your team to find the volume of one of the familiar parts.

Work with your team to find the volume of the remaining part or parts.

Work with your team to find the total volume of the original irregular solid.

a

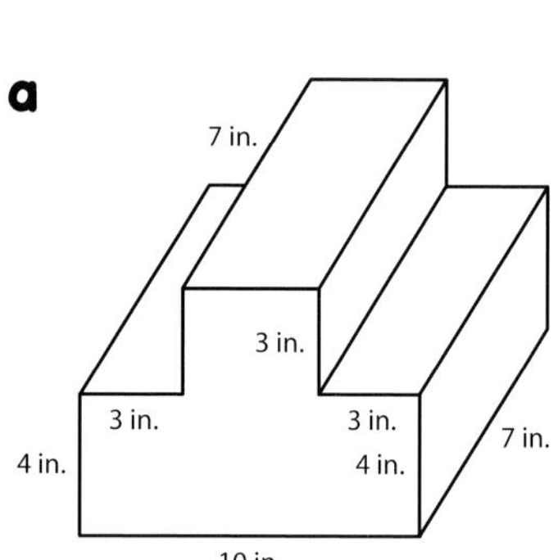

b

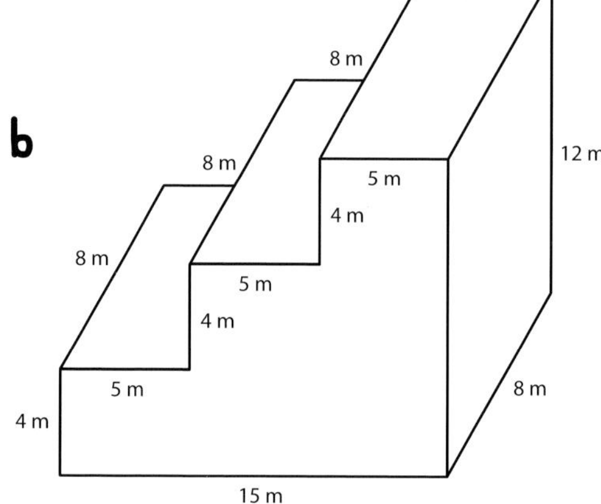

c

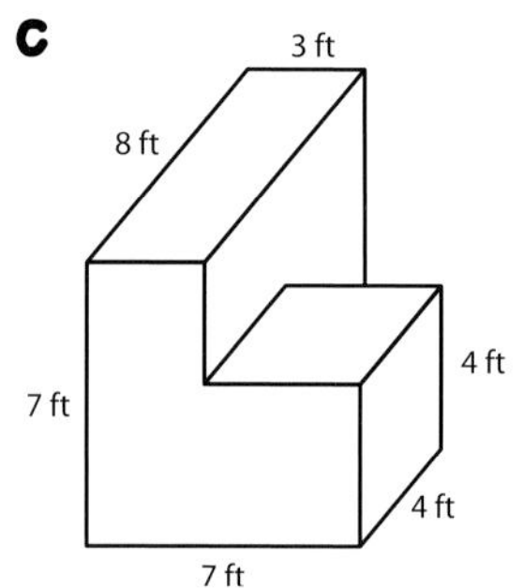

d

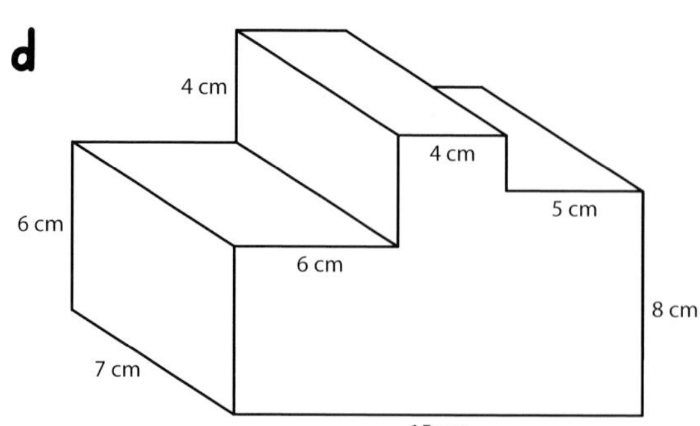

Choose **a**, **b**, **c** or **d**. Discuss whether or not the irregular solid could have been divided into familiar parts in a different way.

Tic Tac Toe

Get Started or

Get 20 squares in one color and 20 in another color.
Get two number cubes for players to share.
Take turns.

For Each Round

Toss the cubes. The numbers you toss are the length and width in inches of a rectangular prism that has a height of 8 inches. Explain how to find the volume of that rectangular prism. Cover the answer. If the answer is taken, lose your turn.

Example

Area of base: 3 in. x 5 in. = 15 in^2
Volume of the rectangular prism: 15 in^2 x 8 in. = 120 in^3

How to Win

The first player or team to cover a row, column, or diagonal in one of the four sections of the game board wins.

24 in^3	160 in^3	48 in^3	144 in^3	80 in^3	40 in^3
200 in^3	96 in^3	8 in^3	240 in^3	32 in^3	160 in^3
80 in^3	40 in^3	120 in^3	48 in^3	16 in^3	72 in^3
144 in^3	96 in^3	64 in^3	24 in^3	288 in^3	96 in^3
16 in^3	48 in^3	240 in^3	128 in^3	64 in^3	32 in^3
96 in^3	192 in^3	32 in^3	120 in^3	48 in^3	192 in^3

If you have more time Play again!

Tic Tac Toe

Get Started Get 20 squares in one color and 20 in another color. Get two number cubes for players to share. Take turns.

For Each Round Toss two cubes. Let your two-digit result be the number of cubic inches in the volume of a rectangular prism. If the height of that rectangular prism is 2 inches, explain how to find the area of its base. Cover the answer. If the answer is taken, lose your turn.

Example Volume of the rectangular prism: **35** cubic inches
Area of its base: **35** $in^3 \div 2$ in $= 17.5\ in^2$

How to Win The first player or team to cover a row, column, or diagonal in one of the four sections of the game board wins.

$6\ in^2$	$30.5\ in^2$	$25.5\ in^2$	$31.5\ in^2$	$22\ in^2$	$11.5\ in^2$
$17\ in^2$	$23\ in^2$	$12.5\ in^2$	$16.5\ in^2$	$13\ in^2$	$22.5\ in^2$
$10.5\ in^2$	$11\ in^2$	$31\ in^2$	$7\ in^2$	$27\ in^2$	$18\ in^2$
$20.5\ in^2$	$15.5\ in^2$	$6.5\ in^2$	$27.5\ in^2$	$32.5\ in^2$	$16\ in^2$
$28\ in^2$	$8\ in^2$	$26.5\ in^2$	$33\ in^2$	$5.5\ in^2$	$17.5\ in^2$
$32\ in^2$	$26\ in^2$	$21\ in^2$	$21.5\ in^2$	$7.5\ in^2$	$12\ in^2$

Play again!

Put 1 2 3 4 in a bag.
Get paper and a pencil.

For Each Round

Choose **A, B, C,** or **D**. Ask someone to read the directions aloud.
Pick a tile. Pick two tiles if your group has only two students. Take turns.
Look at the measurement next to your number.
Discuss: On your turn, explain how to convert to the unit of measurement requested. Find the answer.
Decide: Does your answer make sense? Tell how you know.

A Convert to feet.	
1	**2 mi**
2	**20 yd**
3	**144 in.**
4	**216 in.**

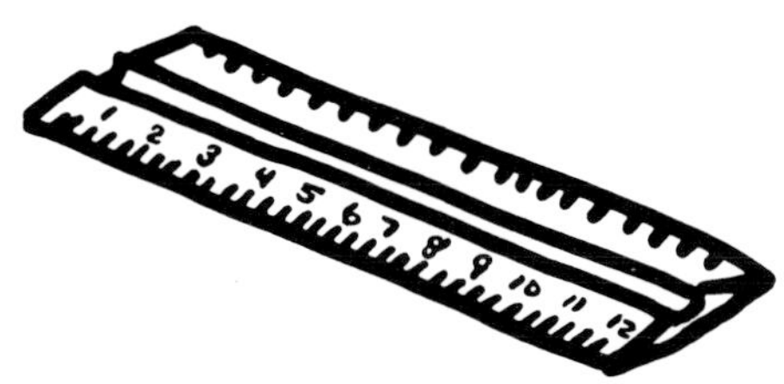

B Convert to miles.	
1	**21,120 ft**
2	**1,760 yd**
3	**253,440 in.**
4	**10,560 ft**

C Convert to yards.	
1	**144 in.**
2	**2 mi**
3	**60 ft**
4	**36 ft**

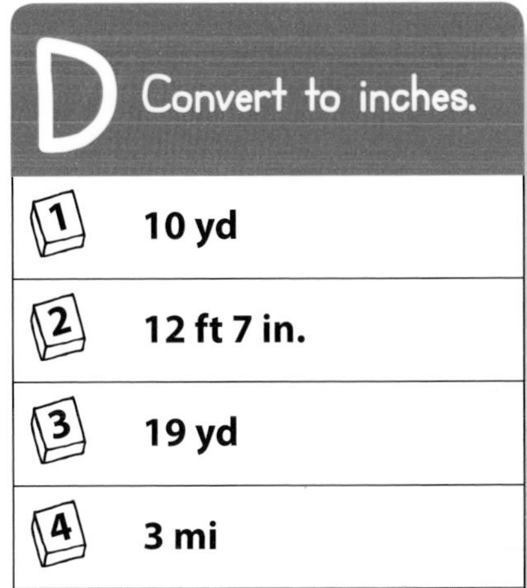

D Convert to inches.	
1	**10 yd**
2	**12 ft 7 in.**
3	**19 yd**
4	**3 mi**

Make up a "Think Together" question about converting units of length. Challenge your classmates to think together to answer your question.

Put 1 2 3 4 in a bag.
Get paper and a pencil.

For Each Round

Choose A, B, C, or D. Ask someone to read the directions aloud.
Pick a tile. Pick two tiles if your group has only two students. Take turns.
Discuss: On your turn, follow the directions using the information next to your tile number.
Decide on an answer. Explain why that answer makes sense.

A Read the conversion process below. From which unit to which other unit can you convert?

1	**Multiply by 12.**
2	**Divide by 3.**
3	**Multiply by 5,280.**
4	**Divide by 12.**

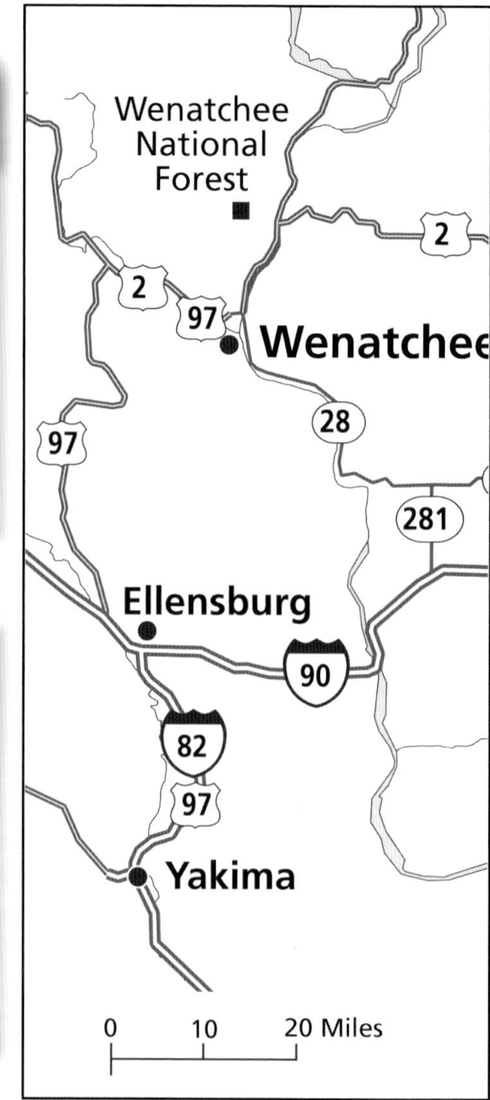

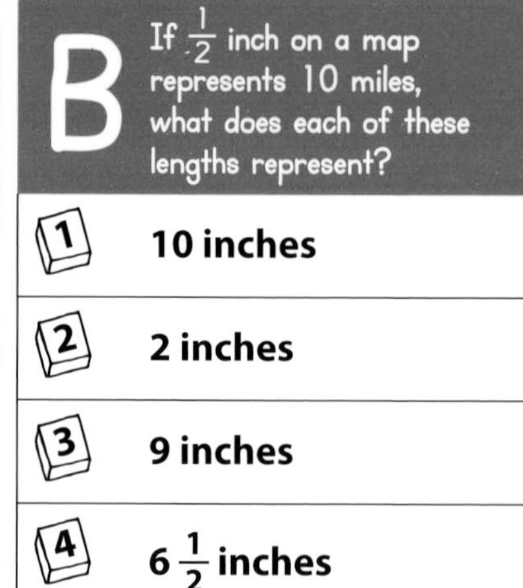

1	**10 inches**
2	**2 inches**
3	**9 inches**
4	**$6\frac{1}{2}$ inches**

C Which is longer? Explain your choice.

1	**An inch or a foot?**
2	**A yard or a mile?**
3	**A foot or a yard?**
4	**A yard or an inch?**

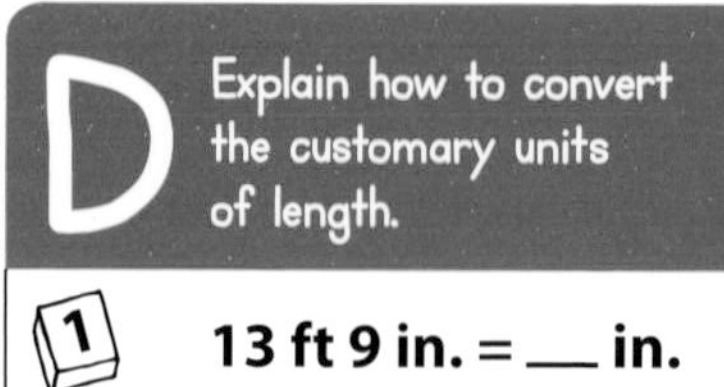

1	**13 ft 9 in. = ___ in.**
2	**58 ft = ___ yd ___ ft**
3	**220 in. = ___ ft ___ in.**
4	**8 mi = ___ in.**

Make up a "Think Together" question about converting units of length. Challenge your classmates to think together to answer your question.

Get Started Get 10 squares in one color and 10 in another color. Get two number cubes. Take turns with another player or team. Talk about math as you play!

At Your Turn Toss two number cubes. Add the dots. Find your toss below. Follow the directions. Explain your thinking. Cover the answer. If the answer is taken, lose your turn. Have fun!

Toss	Explain how to convert each unit of capacity. Look for the missing number on the game board.
2	8 gal = ___ pt
3	30 pt = ___ c
4	8 qt = ___ c
5	8 qt 1 pt = ___ pt
6	10 gal = ___ c
7	1 gal = ___ fl oz
8	64 fl oz = ___ pt
9	128 c = ___ gal
10	60 pt = ___ qt
11	60 qt = ___ gal
12	80 fl oz = ___ c

64	32	4	160
4	17	8	10
160	30	60	17
128	8	128	15

How to Win You win if you are the first to get four connected rectangles, like:

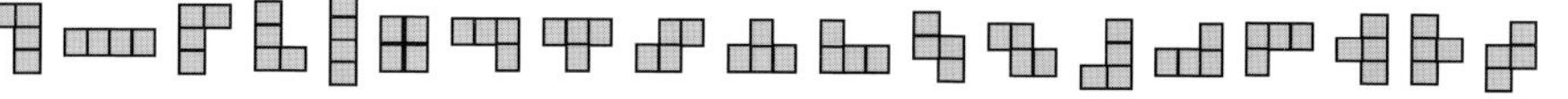

Play again!

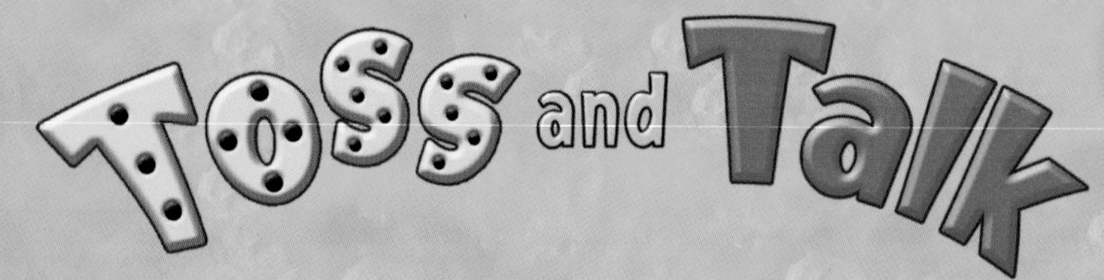

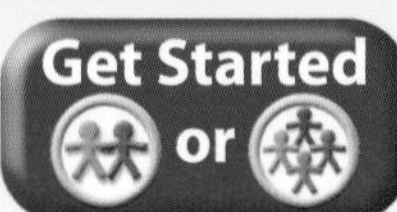

Get 10 squares in one color and 10 in another color.
Get two number cubes. Take turns with another player or team.
Talk about math as you play!

At Your Turn

Toss two number cubes. Add the dots. Find your toss below.
Follow the directions. Explain your thinking. Cover the answer.
If the answer is taken, lose your turn. Have fun!

Toss	Read the capacity next to your toss. Find an equivalent capacity on the game board. Explain your choice.
2	3 c
3	3 qt
4	35 pt
5	48 c
6	64 fl oz
7	160 c
8	80 c
9	10 qt
10	56 fl oz
11	12 c
12	2 c

1 pt	20 qt	24 fl oz	3 gal
6 pt	70 c	4 pt	40 c
20 pt	40 qt	7 c	12 qt
2 qt	5 gal	96 fl oz	10 gal

How to Win

You win if you are the first to get four connected rectangles, like:

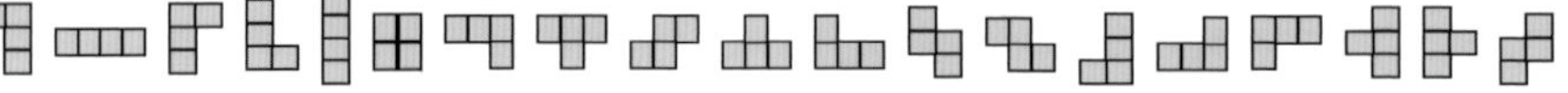

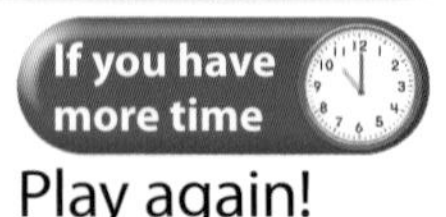

Play again!

Display the Digits

0 1 2 3 4 5 6 7 8 9

Explain how to find each missing number.
Display each 0 – 9 tile exactly once.
If you have a partner, take turns.

a. 320 oz = ☐☐ lb

b. 8,006 lb = ☐ T ☐ lb

c. 80 oz = ☐ lb

d. 48 oz = ☐ lb

e. 224,000 oz = ☐ T

f. 18,000 lb = ☐ T

g. 1 lb 2 oz = ☐☐ oz

Make up equations with missing numbers that involve converting units of weight. Ask your partner to display the missing numbers with tiles.

Display the Digits

0 1 2 3 4 5 6 7 8 9

Read the question. Explain how to find the answer.
Display each 0–9 tile exactly once. If you have a partner, take turns.

Jodie purchases packages of beads for an art project. Each package weighs 8 oz. If she purchases 34 pounds of beads, how many packages does she buy?

[a] [b]

Malik's father is doing some landscaping. He buys 1 T of stones for the rock garden. He uses 1,250 pounds of stones. How many pounds of stones does he have left?

[c] [d] [e]

$4 \text{ oz} = \frac{\boxed{f}}{\boxed{g}} \text{ lb}$

$\frac{1}{1000} \text{ T} = \boxed{h} \text{ lb}$

$48 \text{ oz} = \boxed{i} \text{ lb}$

A healthy baby could weigh 8 lb [j] oz

a	b	c	d	e
f	g	h	i	j

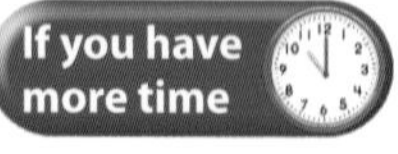

Make up another puzzle about customary units of weight. Ask your partner to display the missing numbers with 0–9 tiles.

Put 1 2 3 4 in a bag.

For Each Round

Choose **A, B, C,** or **D**. Ask someone to read the directions aloud.
Pick a tile. Pick two tiles if your group has only two students. Take turns.
Look at the measurement next to your tile number.
Discuss: On your turn, explain how to convert to the unit of measurement requested. Find the answer.
Decide: Does the answer make sense? Tell how you know.

A	Convert to kilometers.
1	**3,000 m**
2	**150,000,000 mm**
3	**1,000,000 cm**
4	**16,000 m**

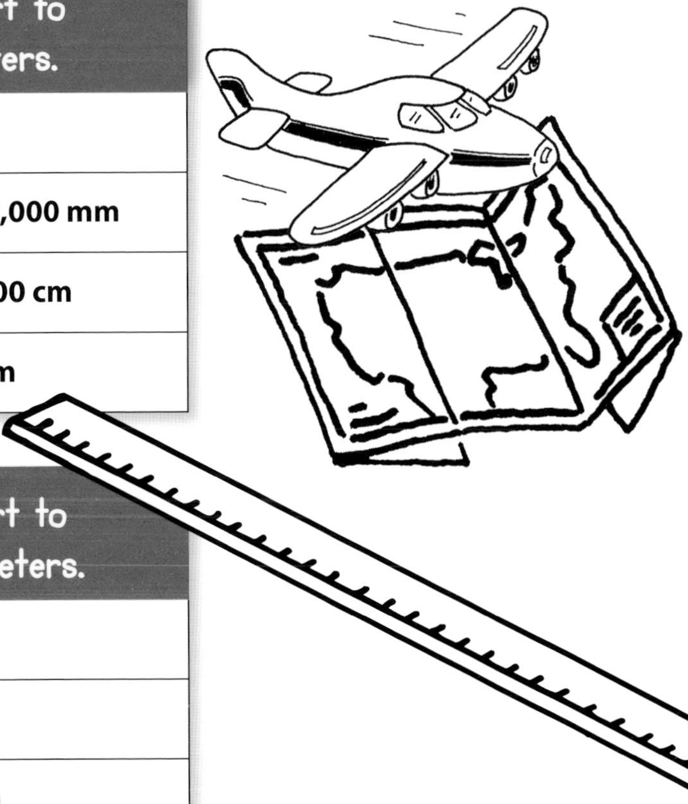

B	Convert to meters.
1	**42,000 mm**
2	**800 km**
3	**102,000 mm**
4	**9,200 cm**

C	Convert to centimeters.
1	**1 km**
2	**1 m**
3	**570 mm**
4	**38 m**

D	Convert to millimeters.
1	**1 km**
2	**1 m**
3	**250 cm**
4	**38 m**

Make up a "Think Together" question about converting units of length. Challenge your classmates to think together to answer your question.

Put 1 2 3 4 in a bag.

For Each Round

Choose A, B, C, or D. Ask someone to read the directions aloud.
Pick a tile. Pick two tiles if your group has only two students. Take turns.
Discuss: On your turn, follow the directions using the information next to your tile number.
Decide on an answer. Explain why that answer makes sense.

A Read the conversion process below. From which unit to which other unit can you convert?

 1	**Multiply by 100.**
 2	**Divide by 1,000.**
 3	**Multiply by 10.**
 4	**Divide by 100.**

kilometer

B If 1 cm on a map represents 20 km, how many kilometers does each of these represent?

 1	**7 cm**
 2	**3.5 cm**
 3	**10.5 cm**
 4	**5.1 cm**

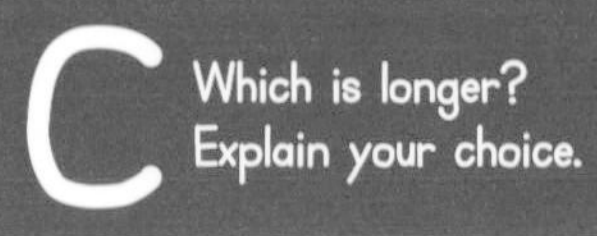

 1	**km or m**
 2	**mm or cm**
 3	**m or cm**
 4	**km or mm**

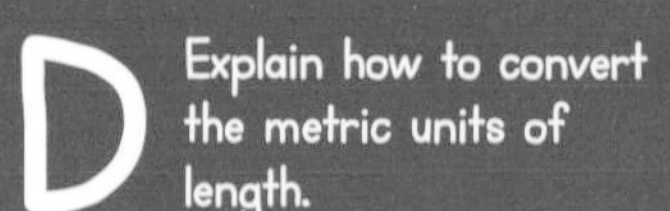

D Explain how to convert the metric units of length.

 1	**4.5 km = ___ m**
 2	**900 m = ___ km**
 3	**1 mm = ___ cm**
 4	**0.5 cm = ___ mm**

Make up a "Think Together" question about converting units of length. Challenge your classmates to think together to answer your question.

Teamwork

Get Started Put 1 2 3 4 in a bag.

Repeat for Each Round Choose **a, b, c, d, e, f, g,** or **h.**
Pick a tile. Pick two tiles if your group has only two students.
Do the jobs listed below in order. To find your job, find the number that matches the tile you chose.

Read the question. Tell your team what you know and what you have to find.

Describe a strategy that you can use to answer the question.

Explain how to find the answer.

Check the answer. Is it correct? How do you know?

a. How do you convert 49,000 milliliters to liters?

b. How do you convert four liters to milliliters?

c. How do you convert 398 liters to milliliters?

d. How do you convert 328,000 milliliters to liters?

e. Which capacity is more reasonable for a bottle of juice? 1 L or 10 mL

f. Which capacity is more reasonable for filling a tank of gas? 40,000 mL or 4L

g. Which capacity is more reasonable for a dose of medicine? 50 mL or 5 L

h. A pitcher holds 2 liters of iced tea. If each person gets 200 mL per serving, how many servings does the pitcher pour?

If you have more time Work as a team. Create more questions like these.
Repeat steps 1 – 4 for your questions.

Teamwork

Get Started Put 1 2 3 4 in a bag.

Repeat for Each Round Choose **a, b, c, d, e,** or **f**.
Pick a tile. Pick two tiles if your group has only two students.
Do the jobs listed below in order. To find your job, find the number that matches the tile you chose.

Explain how to compare the two capacities.

Would you place >, <, or = between the two capacities?
Read the comparison using <, >, or =.
Explain why the comparison makes sense.

Name an item that might have the capacity listed on the left.

Name an item that might have the capacity listed on the right.

a	2 L ◯ 200 mL	b	1 L ◯ 1,000 mL
c	330 mL ◯ 3 L	d	4 L ◯ 4,500 mL
e	2.5 L ◯ 2,500 mL	f	1 mL ◯ 1 L

If you have more time Choose two capacities for your team.
Repeat steps 1 – 4 for your capacities.

Display the Digits

0 1 2 3 4 5 6 7 8 9

Explain how to find each missing number.
Display each 0–9 tile exactly once.
If you have a partner, take turns.

a. 28,000 g = ☐☐ kg

b. Which is greater, 43 g or 76 mg? ☐☐

c. 10,000,000 mg = ☐☐ kg

d. 97,000 g = ☐☐ kg

e. 56,000 mg = ☐☐ g

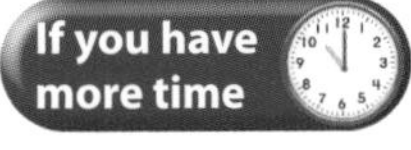

Make up another puzzle about converting metric units of mass.
Ask your partner to display the answers with 0–9 tiles.

Display the Digits

0 1 2 3 4 5 6 7 8 9

Explain how to find each missing number.
Display each 0–9 tile exactly once.
If you have a partner, take turns.

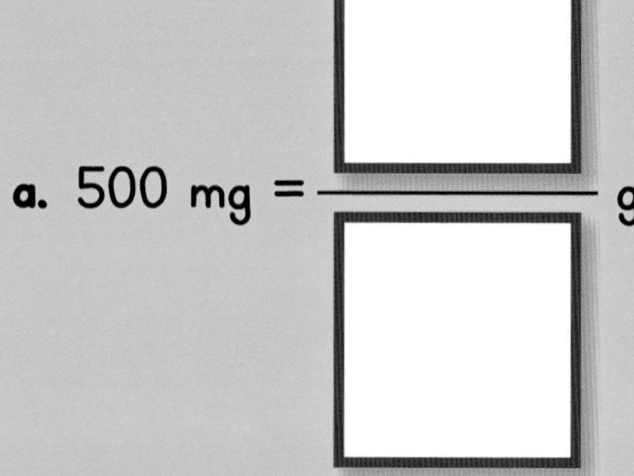

a. 500 mg = $\frac{\square}{\square}$ g

b. A nickel might weigh  g,

Hint: 200 nickels weigh about a kilogram.

c. Kendall is beginning a science experiment in the lab. The instructions call for 214 milligrams of potassium. What is the difference between this amount and 1 gram?

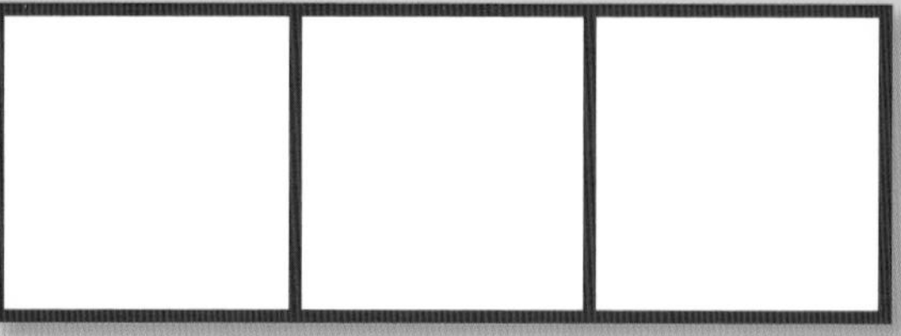 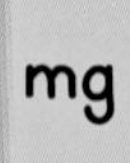 mg

d. $\frac{9}{100}$ kg = ☐☐ g

e. 34,000 mg =  g

Make up another puzzle about converting metric units of mass.
Ask your partner to display the answers with 0–9 tiles.

Teamwork

Get paper and pencil
Put 1 2 3 4 in a bag.

Choose problem **a** or **b**. Ask someone to read the problem aloud.
Pick a tile. Pick two tiles if your group has only two students.
Ask and answer the questions listed below in order.
To find your question, find the number that matches the tile you chose.

 **What are the different possible lengths and widths of the garden if you use only whole numbers?**

 **What are the different possible areas of the garden?**

 **What are the dimensions of the garden with the greatest area? What are the dimensions of the garden with the least area?**

 **What is the answer to the question in the problem?**

a. John wants to fence in a rectangular piece of land with 36 yards of fencing. Each 1-foot by 3-foot patch can yield one watermelon. What is the greatest number of watermelons John can have?

b. Mary wants to plant tomatoes in a rectangular garden. Each plant should take a 9-inch by 9-inch square. She has a fence 34 feet long to put around her garden. What is the greatest number of tomato plants that she can plant?

Make up another problem that involves multiple steps.
Ask a partner to solve your problem.

Teamwork

Get Started or

Get paper and pencil
Put 1 2 3 4 in a bag.

Repeat for Each Round

Choose problem **a** or **b**. Ask someone to read the problem aloud.
Pick a tile. Pick two tiles if your group has only two students.
Do the jobs listed below in order.
To find your job, find the number that matches the tile you chose.

What are the different possible lengths and widths of the land if you use only whole numbers?

What are the different possible perimeters of the land?

What are the dimensions of the land with the greatest perimeter? What are the dimensions of the land with the least perimeter?

What is the answer to the question in the problem?

a. Susan wants to put a fence around a rectangular piece of land with an area of 100 square feet. Fencing costs $10 per foot. What is the greatest and the least amount she could pay? Explain your answer.

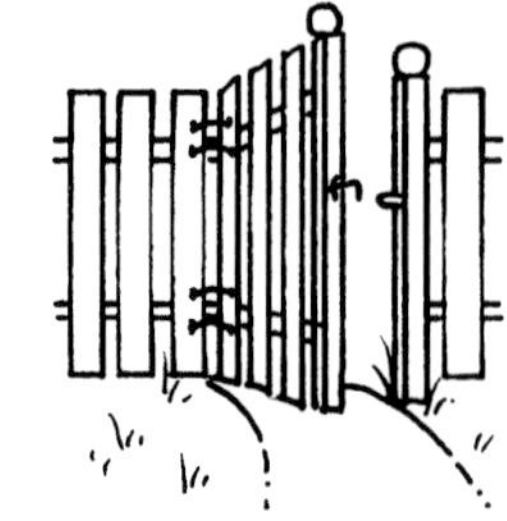

b. Tom and Alice agree to run a race at the same time around two different rectangular tracks. Each track surrounds a different field. The area of each field is 350 square yards. Tom's rectangular track is 5 yards by 70 yards. Both runners run at the same speed. Alice finishes the race in a little more than half of Tom's time. How can this be? Explain your answer.

Make up another problem that involves multiple steps.
Ask a partner to solve your problem.

Teamwork

Get paper and a pencil.
Put 1 2 3 4 in a bag.

Repeat for Each Round

Choose **a**, **b**, **c**, or **d**.
Pick a tile. Pick two tiles if your group has only two students.
Do the jobs listed below in order.
To find your job, find the number that matches the tile you chose.

 **Read the title and the data to your group.**

 **Draw a line plot for the data.**

 **Using the line plot created in Step 2, identify any outliers.**

 **Answer the question below the data. Ask your team members if they agree with your answer.**

a

Student Test Scores
95, 95, 90, 100, 70, 95, 100, 90, 85, 90, 90, 100

Which test score occurred most often?

b

Students' Shoe Sizes
6, 7, 7, 8, 9, 8, 9, 9, 13

What is the range of the students' shoe sizes?

c

Number of Minutes Spent on Homework
25, 30, 20, 20, 20, 25, 30, 35, 20, 60

How many students spent more than 20 minutes on homework?

d

Number of Points Scored During Each Soccer Game
0, 2, 2, 0, 1, 1, 1, 1, 1, 10

Which game score occurred most often?

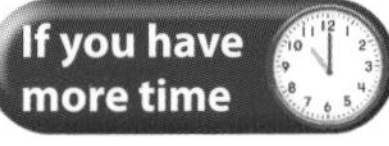

Create a survey question like **b** or **c**. Survey your classmates.
Record the results in a line plot. Identify any outliers.

Teamwork

Get 0 1 2 3 4 5 6 7.

Repeat for Each Round Take turns. Read a question. Use number tiles to answer the question. Use each number tile exactly once.

Hours Spent Playing on Saturday
Grade 4 Students

Number of Hours	1	2	3	4	5
	X X X X	X X X X X	X X X X X X	X X X	X X

Number of Hours

[a] students play for 4 or more hours.

There are [b][c] students in grade 4.

[d][e] students played for 2, 3, or 4 hours.

[f] more students played for 3 hours than for 4 hours.

[g] students played for 1 hour or 4 hours.

[h] students played for 3 hours.

a	b	c	d
e	f	g	h

Take turns with a partner. On your turn, make up a question based on the data in the line plot. Ask your partner to answer your question.

Teamwork

Get paper and pencil.
Put 1 2 3 in a bag.

Repeat for Each Round

Choose **A** or **B**.
Pick a tile. Do the jobs listed below in order.
To find your job, find the number that matches the tile you chose.

Look at the line plot. Make an observation about the data.

Decide what survey question might have been asked. Make sure the question is worded clearly.

Make a frequency table that shows the same results as the line plot.

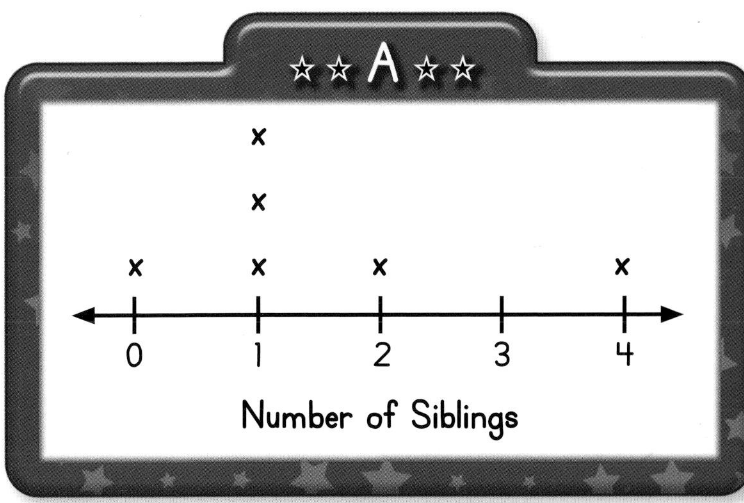

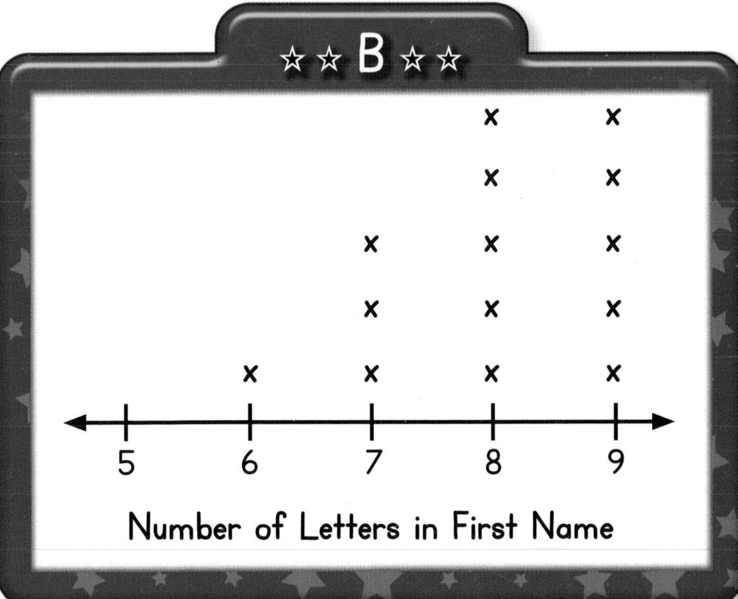

Create a survey question of your own. Poll your classmates.
Draw a line plot for your data and repeat steps 1 – 4.

Teamwork

Get paper and pencil.
Put 1 2 3 4 in a bag.

Repeat for Each Round

Choose A or B.
Pick a tile. Pick two tiles if your group has only two students.
Do the jobs listed below in order. To find your job, find the number that matches the tile you chose.

 **Look at the set of data. Decide what the data could represent.**

 **Create a line plot for the data.**

 **Make a frequency table for the data.**

 **Compare the line plot and the frequency table. Discuss what they have in common. Describe their differences.**

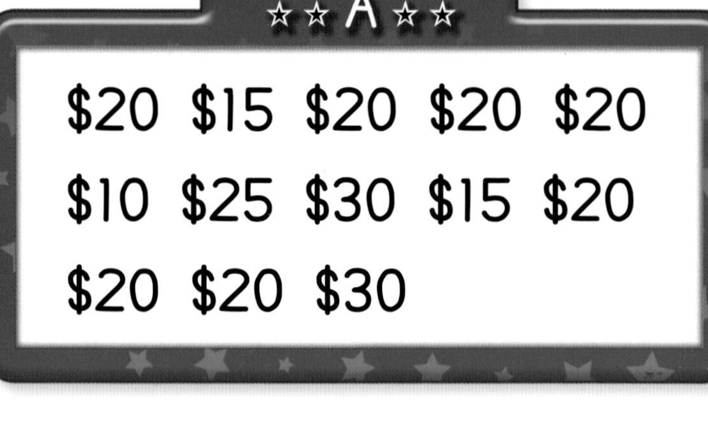

B

95% 100% 100% 100%
90% 85% 90% 100%
95% 100% 90%

Create a set of data. Repeat steps 1 – 4 for your data.

Display the Digits

0 1 2 3 4 5 6 7 8 9

Read a question. Explain how to use the line plot to answer the question. Display each 0 – 9 tile exactly once. If you have a partner, take turns.

Twenty-five third graders had 20 new spelling words to learn. The results are shown on the line plot.

How many students spelled 16 or 18 words correctly? [a]

A student is most likely to spell [b] words correctly.

[1] 14 [2] 16 [3] 18 [4] 20

Only one student spelled exactly [c] words correctly.

[1] 14 [2] 15 [3] 17 [4] 19

How many students spelled 21 words correctly? [d]

How many students spelled 16 words correctly? [e]

Results of Spelling New Words Correctly

Number of New Words Spelled Correctly	14	15	16	17	18	19	20
	xxx	x	xxxxx	xx	xxxx	xxx	xxxxxxx

This line plot shows how many days third grade students spent at summer camp.

How many students went to summer camp? [f][g]

A student is most likely to spend [h] days in summer camp.

How many students spent 5 or 7 days at camp? 1[i]

How many more students spent 5 days at camp than those staying 9 days? [j]

Third Grade Students' Days at Summer Camp

Number of Days	3	5	7	9	11
	xxx	xxxxxxxx	xxxxxxxxxx	xxxxxxx	xxxxxxxx

a	b	c	d	e
f	g	h	i	j

Make up other questions about the data in one of the line plots. Ask your partner to display the answers with 0 – 9 tiles.

Center Activity **14-3**

Display the Digits

0 1 2 3 4 5 6 7 8 9

Get paper and a pencil. For each set of data, make a line plot and then answer each question. Display each 0 – 9 tile exactly once. If you have a partner, take turns.

Every student in two third grade classes voted on a favorite type of cereal. The following numbers of students voted for each type of cereal: 16 corn cereal, 8 bran cereal, 12 rice cereal, 14 oat cereal, and 15 wheat cereal.

How many students are in the two third grade classes? [a][b]

A student is most likely to choose which cereal? [c]

[1] corn cereal [2] rice cereal
[3] oat cereal [4] wheat cereal

How many more students voted for corn cereal than bran cereal? [d]

How many students voted for oat cereal or wheat cereal? [e][f]

Data was collected from 52 fourth graders about their favorite dinner. The results were: 22 voted for pizza, 15 voted for spaghetti, 10 voted for chicken, and 5 voted for tacos.

A student is least likely to choose which dinner? [g]

[1] pizza [2] spaghetti
[3] chicken [4] tacos

How many students voted for spaghetti, chicken, or tacos? [h][i]

How many more students voted for pizza than for spaghetti? [j]

a	b	c	d	e
f	g	h	i	j

Make up other questions about one of your line plots. Ask your partner to display the answers with 0 – 9 tiles.

Teamwork

Get paper and a pencil.
Put 1 2 3 4 in a bag.

Choose **a**, **b**, **c**, or **d**.
Pick a tile. Pick two tiles if your group has only two students.
Do the jobs listed below in order.
To find your job, find the number that matches the tile you chose.

 **Read the title and the data to your group.**

 **Draw a line plot for the data.**

 **Using the line plot created in Step 2, identify any outliers.**

 **Answer the question below the data. Ask your team members if they agree with your answer.**

a

Student Test Scores

85, 95, 90, 100, 70, 95, 100, 90, 85, 90, 90, 85

Which test score occurred most often?

b

Students' Shoe Sizes

6, 7, 7, 8, 8, 9, 8, 9, 10, 9, 13

What is the range of the students' shoe sizes?

c

Number of Minutes Spent on Homework

25, 30, 20, 20, 20, 25, 30, 35, 20, 60

How many students spent more than 20 minutes on homework?

d

Number of Points Scored During Each Soccer Game

0, 2, 2, 3, 0, 1, 1, 1, 5, 1, 1, 10

Which game score occurred most often?

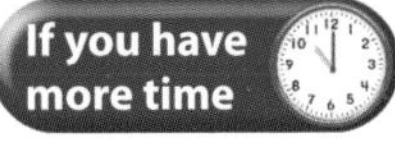

Create a survey question like **b** or **c**. Survey your classmates. Record the results in a line plot. Identify any outliers.

Teamwork

Get 0 1 2 3 4 5 6 7.

Repeat for Each Round

Take turns. Read a question. Use number tiles to answer the question. Use each number tile exactly once.

Hours Spent Playing on Saturday
Grade 5 Students

Number of Hours	1	2	3	4	5
Students	XXXX	XXXXX	XXXXXXX	XXX	XX

There are [a][b] students in grade 5.

[c] students play for 4 or more hours.

[d][e] students played for 2, 3, or 4 hours.

[f] more students played for 3 hours than for 4 hours.

[g] students played for 3 hours.

[h] students played for 1 hour or 4 hours.

a	b	c	d
e	f	g	h

Take turns with a partner. On your turn, make up a question based on the data in the line plot. Ask your partner to answer your question.

Teamwork

Get paper and a pencil (optional).
Put 1 2 3 4 in a bag.

Repeat for Each Round

Choose **A, B, C,** or **D**. Let someone read the name of the graph.
Pick a tile. Pick two tiles if your group has only two students.
Do the jobs listed below in order. To find your job, find the number that matches the tile you chose.

A

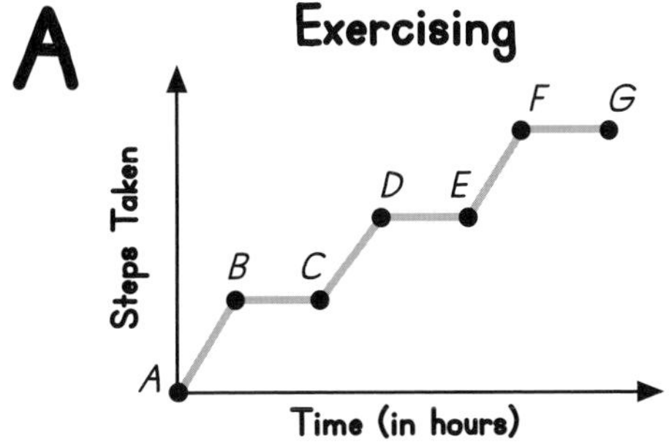

B

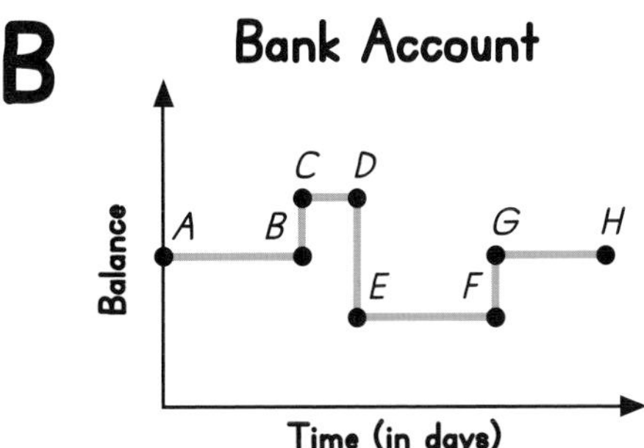

C

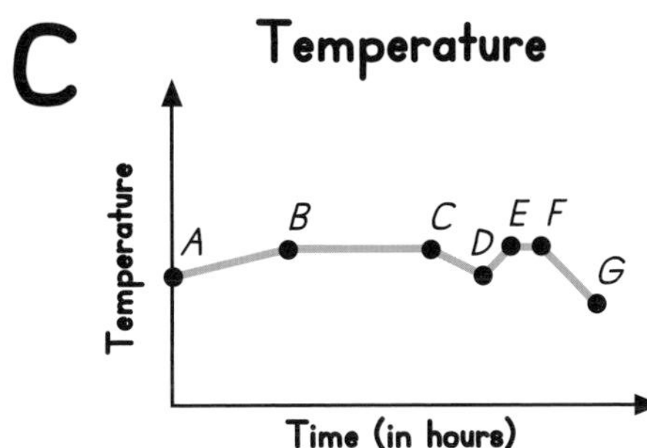

D

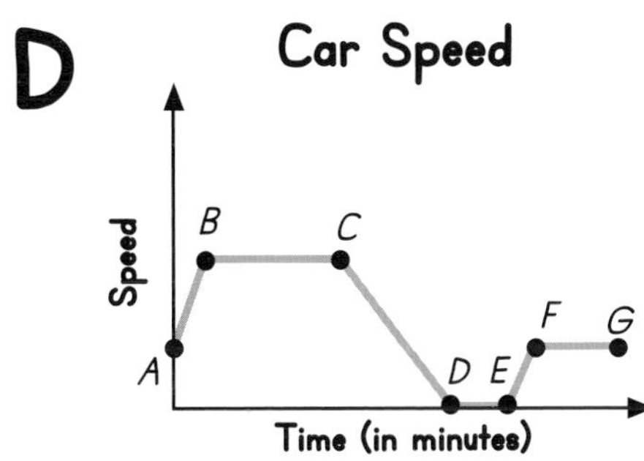

Do the Jobs Listed Below in Order

 **Describe what the graph shows**

 **Describe the situation for each point on the graph.**

 **Describe the situation for the highest and lowest points on the graph.**

 **Write or tell a story described by the graph. Explain each point.**

Put the number tiles back in the bag. Draw tiles to find your next jobs.
Choose a different graph. Repeat steps 1–4.

Teamwork

Get paper, pencil, and a ruler.
Put 1 2 3 4 in a bag.

Repeat for Each Round

Choose **A, B, C,** or **D**. Let someone read the phrase that describes a situation. Work as a team to construct a graph for that situation. Pick a tile. Pick two tiles if your group has only two students. Do the jobs listed below in order. To find your job, find the number that matches the tile you chose.

A Your height above the ground as you ride a roller coaster

B Your distance from the ground as you ride a Ferris wheel

C Your speed as you ride a bicycle from home to school and back

D Your distance as you walk your dog from home to the park and back

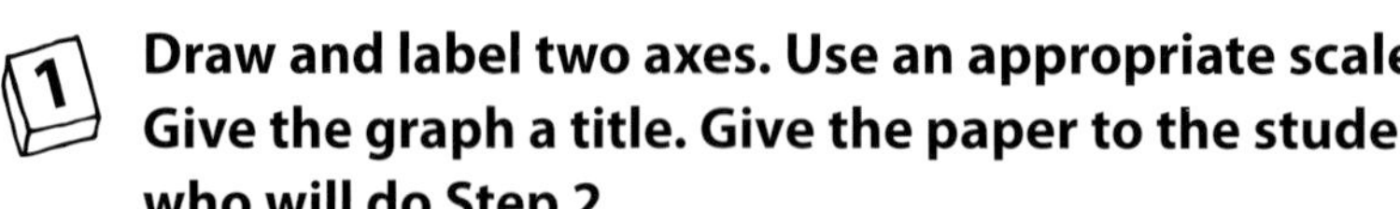

1. **Draw and label two axes. Use an appropriate scale. Give the graph a title. Give the paper to the student who will do Step 2.**
2. **Sketch the first half of the graph. Explain each point. Give the paper to the student who will do Step 3.**
3. **Sketch the second half of the graph. Explain each point. Give the paper to the student who will do Step 4.**
4. **Write or tell a story described by the graph.**

Put the number tiles back in the bag. Draw tiles to find your next jobs. Choose a different graph. Repeat steps 1–4.

Teamwork

Put 1 2 3 4 in a bag.

Repeat for Each Round

Choose a, b, c, d, e, or f.
Pick a tile. Pick two tiles if your group has only two students.
Do the jobs listed below in order.
To find your job, find the number that matches the tile you chose.

1. **Tell whether the figure is a polygon. Give your reason.**
2. **Give the number of sides and vertices if the figure is a polygon.**
3. **If the figure is a polygon, name that polygon.**
4. **Decide if the figure is a regular polygon. Give your reason.**

a

b

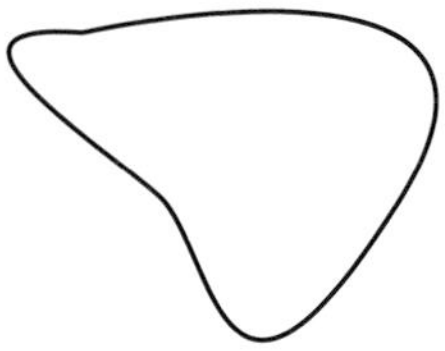

c

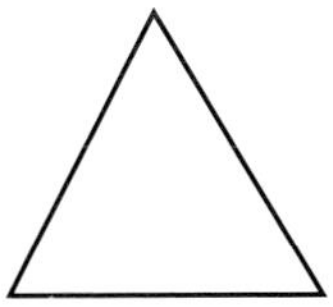

d

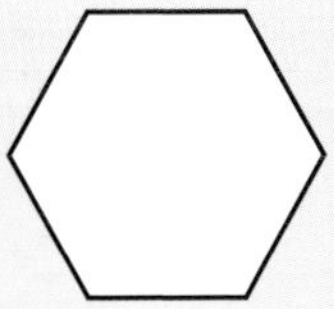

e

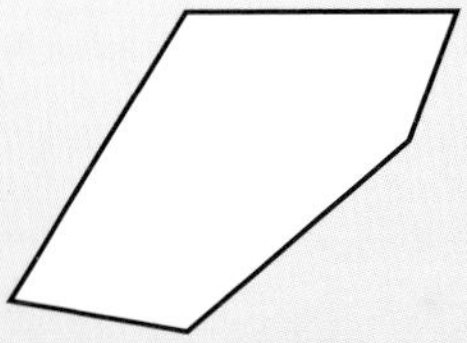

f

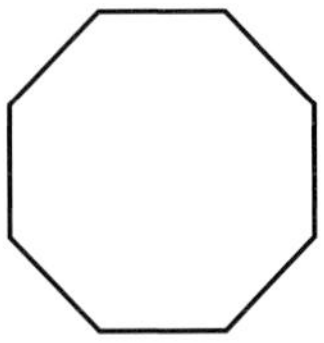

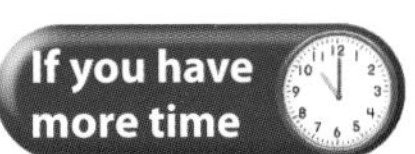

Draw other shapes. Repeat steps 1 – 4 for your shapes.

Teamwork

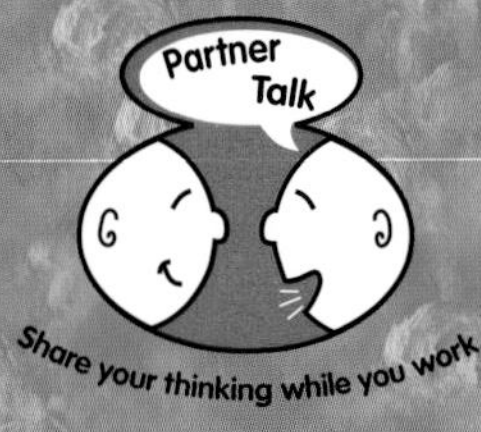

Put 1 2 3 4 in a bag.

Repeat for Each Round

Choose a, b, c, d, e, or f.
Pick a tile. Pick two tiles if your group has only two students.
Do the jobs listed below in order.
To find your job, find the number that matches the tile you chose.

 **State whether the figure is a polygon. Give your reason.**

 **Give the number of sides and vertices if the figure is a polygon.**

 **Decide if the figure is a regular polygon. Give your reason.**

 **If the figure is a regular polygon, name that polygon.**

a

b

c

d

e

f

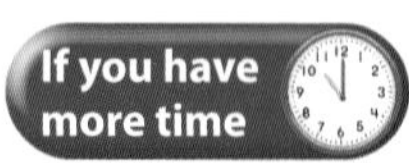

Draw other shapes.
Repeat steps 1 – 4 for your shapes.

Get 10 squares in one color and 10 in another color.
Get two number cubes. Take turns with another player or team.
Remember, the sum of the angles in a triangle is 180°

At Your Turn

Toss two number cubes. Add the dots. Find your toss below.
Follow the directions. Explain your thinking. Cover the answer.
If the answer is taken, lose your turn. Have fun!

Toss	Explain how to find the missing measure of the third angle if the other two angles in a triangle have these measures.
2	? 60° 30°
3	? 65° 45°
4	60° 60° ?
5	? 47° 65°
6	90° ? 53°
7	? 37° 95°
8	84° 58° ?
9	28° 75° ?
10	45° ? 55°
11	? 50° 30°
12	45° ? 90°

100°	48°	77°	60°
90°	68°	80°	38°
77°	37°	68°	48°
45°	38°	37°	70°

How to Win

You win if you are the first to get four connected rectangles, like:

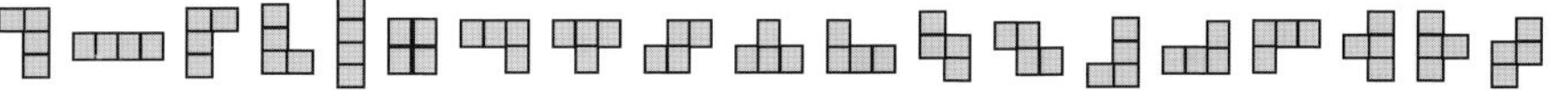

Play again!

Get 10 squares in one color and 10 in another color.
Get two number cubes. Take turns with another player or team.
Remember, the sum of the angles in a triangle is 180°

At Your Turn

Toss two number cubes. Add the dots. Find your toss below.
Follow the directions. Explain your thinking. Cover the answer.
If the answer is taken, lose your turn. Have fun!

Toss	The measure of one angle in a triangle is given. Find the measures of two other angles that could be in that triangle.
2	60°
3	63°
4	70°
5	39°
6	77°

7	97°
8	28°
9	49°
10	64°
11	45°
12	80°

34°, 97°, ____	58°, ____, 83°	36°, 80°, ____	45°, 38°, ____
____, 29°, 74°	____, 45°, 90°	96°, ____, 56°	72°, 59°, ____
73°, ____, 79°	50°, 50°, ____	30°, ____, 90°	47°, ____, 94°
40°, 43°, ____	58°, 59°, ____	____, 36°, 67°	25°, ____, 85°

How to Win

You win if you are the first to get four connected rectangles, like:

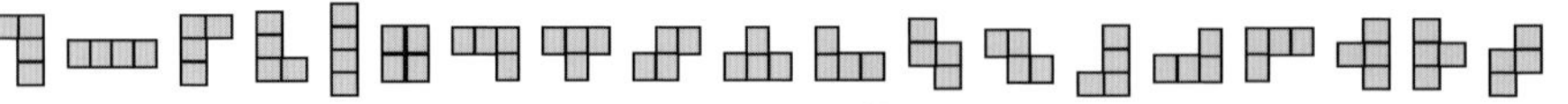

Play again!

Teamwork

Partner Talk
Share your thinking while you work.

Get Started

Get 5 squares in one color for one team.
Get 5 squares in another color for the other team.
Put 1 2 3 4 5 6 7 8 9 in a bag.
Form two teams of two.

Repeat for Each Round

Pick a tile. Find the name of a quadrilateral next to that number.
Find the definition or an example of that quadrilateral on the game board.
Cover your answer with a square. Lose your turn if you cannot find the definition or an example. Set the tile aside. Repeat until one team gets three squares in one row, column, or diagonal.

1 **Rectangle**  **Rhombus**  **Parallelogram**

 **Trapezoid**  **Square**  **Trapezoid**

 **Parallelogram**  **Rectangle**  **Rhombus**

a parallelogram with four right angles	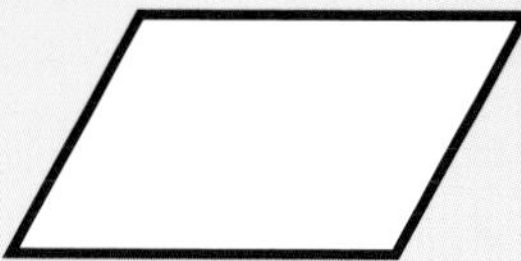	a quadrilateral with only one pair of parallel sides
		a parallelogram with all sides the same length
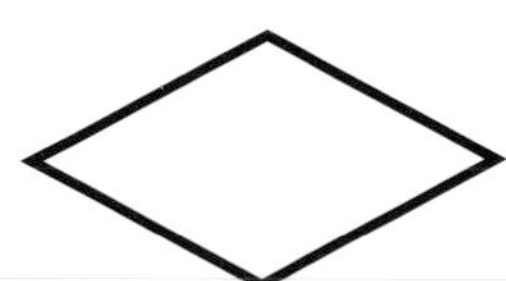	a quadrilateral with both pairs of opposite sides parallel and equal in length	

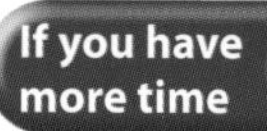

Play again!

Teamwork

Get Started

Get 5 squares in one color for one team.
Get 5 squares in another color for the other team.
Put 1 2 3 4 5 6 7 8 9 in a bag.
Form two teams of two.

Repeat for Each Round

Pick a tile. Find three angle measures next to your tile number.
Given those three angle measures of a quadrilateral, find the measure of the fourth angle on the game board. Use a square to cover your answer.
Set the tile aside. Repeat until one team gets three squares in one row, column, or diagonal.

 **45°, 85°, 85°, ____**

 120° ? 60° 70°

3 **63°, 138°, 42°, ____**

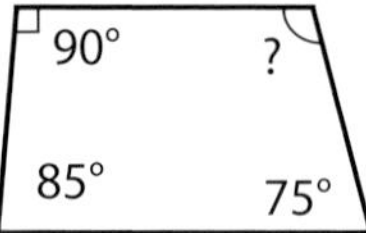

 **115°, 80°, 115°, ____**

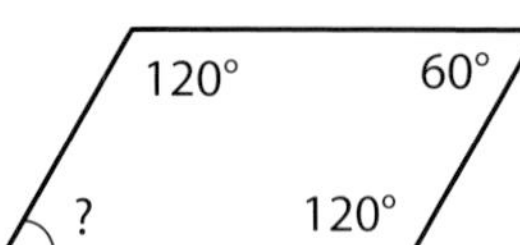

 **90°, 90°, 95°, ____**

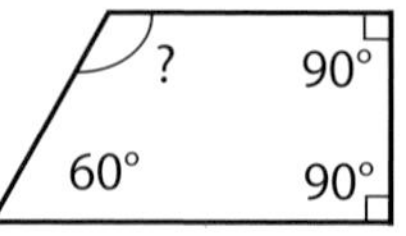

 **95°, 85°, 80°, ____**

85°	110°	50°
120°	60°	100°
110°	117°	145°

Hint: the sum of the angles in a quadrilateral is 360°

If you have more time Play again!

Get Started 

Get 10 squares in one color and 10 in another color.
Get two number cubes. Take turns with another player or team.
Talk about math as you play!

At Your Turn

Toss two number cubes. Add the dots. Find your toss below.
Follow the directions. Explain your thinking. Cover the answer.
If the answer is taken, lose your turn. Have fun!

Toss	Describe the shape. Match your description with a word or phrase on the game board.
2	
3	
4	
5	
6	
7	
8	
9	
10	
11	
12	

Rectangle	Quadrilateral with no parallel sides	Rhombus	Trapezoid
Parallelogram with no right angles	Trapezoid	Rhombus	Parallelogram with no right angles
Rhombus	Square	Rectangle	Quadrilateral with no parallel sides
Trapezoid	Square	Quadrilateral with no parallel sides	Parallelogram with no right angles

How to Win

You win if you are the first to get four connected rectangles, like:

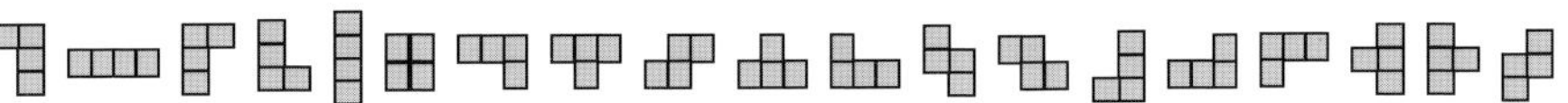

Play again!

Toss and Talk

Get 10 squares in one color and 10 in another color.
Get two number cubes. Take turns with another player or team.
Talk about math as you play!

At Your Turn

Toss two number cubes. Add the dots. Find your toss below.
Follow the directions. Explain your thinking. Cover the answer.
If the answer is taken, lose your turn. Have fun!

Toss	Read the directions. Look for that polygon on the game board. If you find it, explain your choice.
2	Find a quadrilateral that is not a trapezoid or a parallelogram.
3	Find a quadrilateral that has two parallel sides and is not a parallelogram.
4	Find a quadrilateral that has equal opposite sides, but has no right angles.
5	Find a quadrilateral that is a parallelogram, but not a rectangle or a rhombus.
6	Find a rhombus that is not a square.
7	Find a parallelogram that is not a square but has four right angles.
8	Find a parallelogram that is both a rhombus and a rectangle.
9	Find a quadrilateral that has no equal sides.
10	Find a quadrilateral with four equal sides that is not a square.
11	Find a parallelogram that has no right angles and is not a rhombus.
12	Find a parallelogram with equal sides and four right angles.

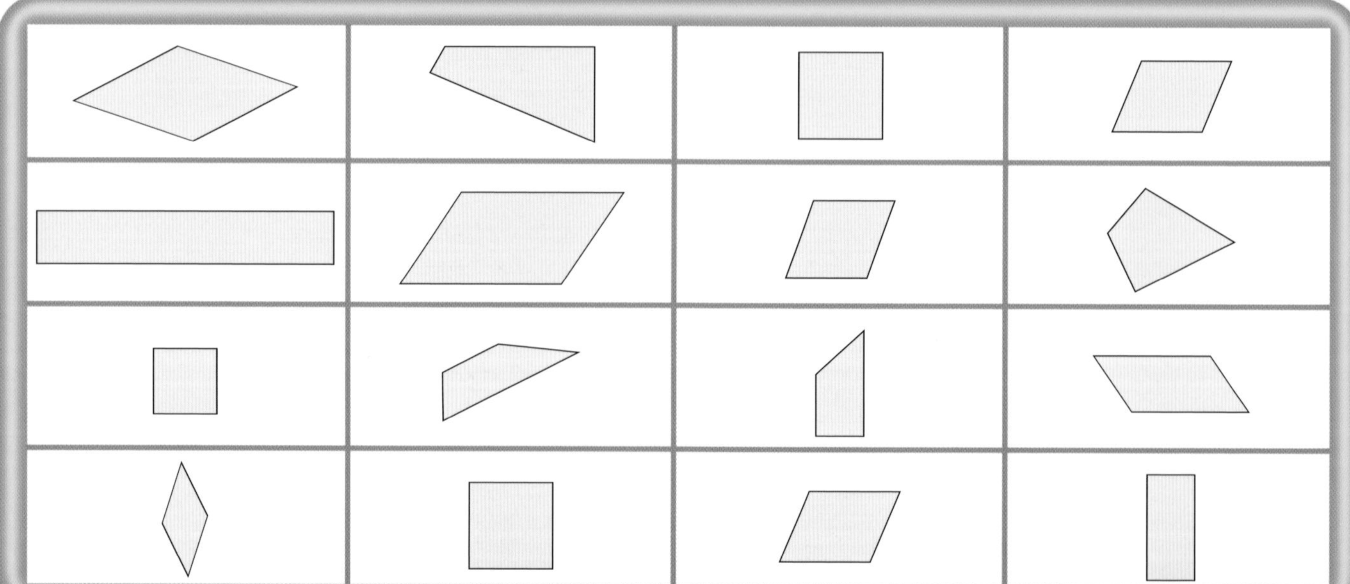

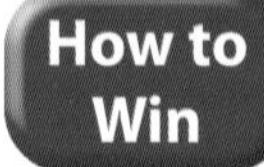

You win if you are the first to get four connected rectangles, like:

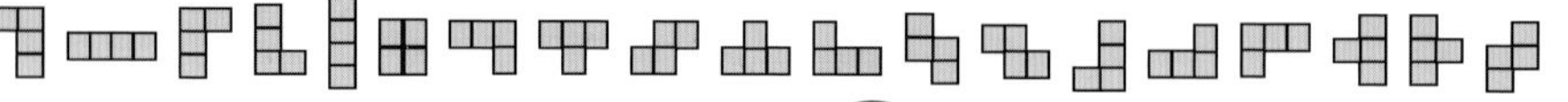

Play again!

Think Together

Put 1 2 3 4 in a bag.

For Each Round

Choose A, B, C, D, E, or F.
Pick a tile. Pick two tiles if your group has only two students.
Tell your group if the word next to your number names the shape.
Discuss: Which three names describe the geometric figure? Why?
Decide: Which name does not describe the figure? Why not?

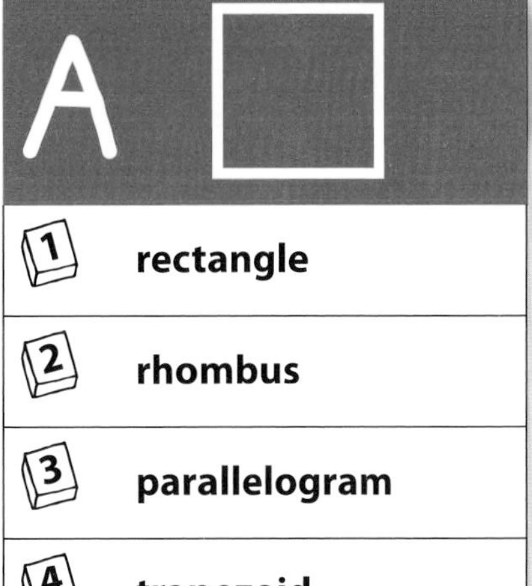

	A
1	rectangle
2	rhombus
3	parallelogram
4	trapezoid

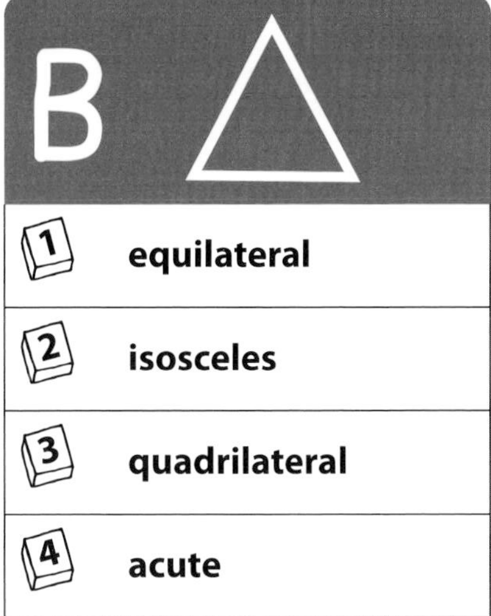

	B
1	equilateral
2	isosceles
3	quadrilateral
4	acute

	C
1	quadrilateral
2	parallelogram
3	rectangle
4	rhombus

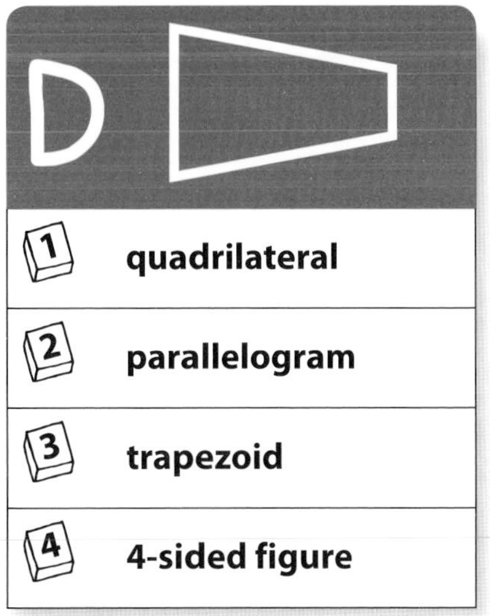

	D
1	quadrilateral
2	parallelogram
3	trapezoid
4	4-sided figure

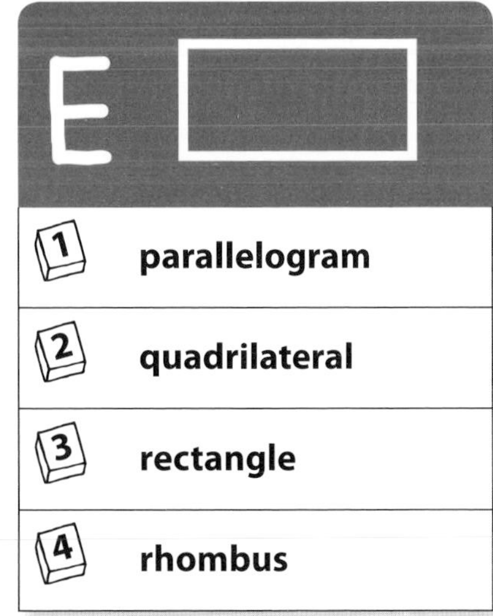

	E
1	parallelogram
2	quadrilateral
3	rectangle
4	rhombus

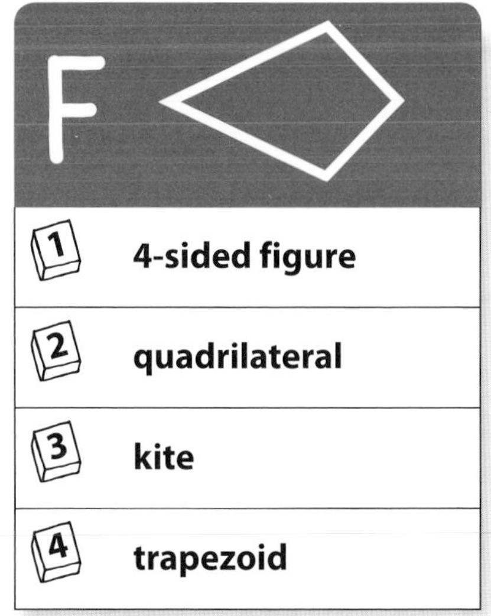

	F
1	4-sided figure
2	quadrilateral
3	kite
4	trapezoid

Make up a "Think Together" question about quadrilaterals.
Challenge your classmates to think together to answer your question.

Think Together

Put 1 2 3 4 in a bag.

For Each Round

Choose A, B, C, D, E, or **F**.
Pick a tile. Pick two tiles if your group has only two students.
Answer the question for the shape next to your number.
Discuss: Which three shapes have the given name? Why?
Decide: Which shape does not have the given name? Why not?

A Is the shape a quadrilateral? Why or why not?

1, 2, 3, 4

B Is the shape a trapezoid? Why or why not?

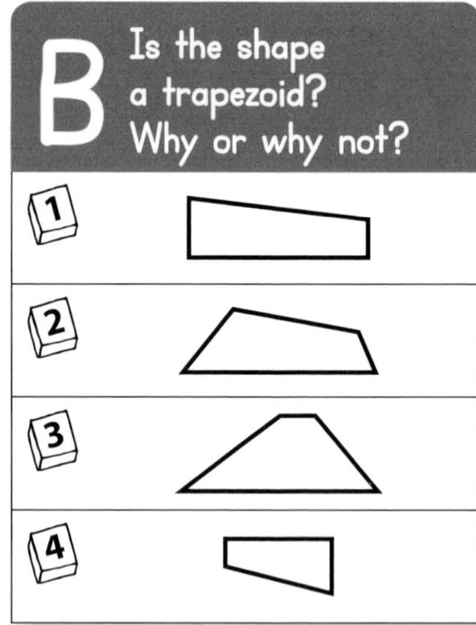

C Is the shape a parallelogram? Why or why not?

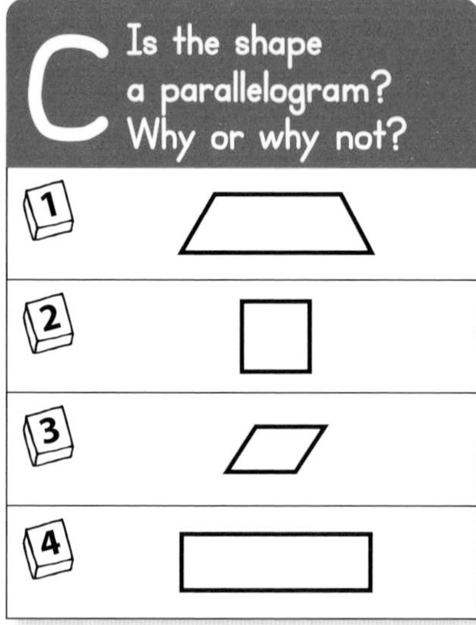

D Is the shape a rectangle? Why or why not?

1, 2, 3, 4

E Is the shape a rhombus? Why or why not?

1, 2, 3, 4

F Is the shape a square? Why or why not?

1, 2, 3, 4

If you have more time Make up a "Think Together" question about quadrilaterals. Challenge your classmates to think together to answer your question.

Put 1 2 3 4 in a bag.

For Each Round

Choose A, B, C, D, E, or F.
Pick a tile. Pick two tiles if your group has only two students.
Determine whether the words next to your tile number complete the sentence to make a true statement or a false statement.
Discuss: Which three endings make the sentence false? Why?
Decide: Which ending makes the statement true? Why?

A No composite number has	
1	three prime factors.
2	only one prime factor.
3	all even factors.
4	one even and one odd factor.

B No rectangle has	
1	all sides congruent.
2	congruent diagonals.
3	the measures of its interior angles totaling 180°.
4	all angles congruent.

C No perfect square number	
1	has exactly four factors.
2	is even.
3	is neither prime nor composite.
4	has both an even and an odd factor.

D No parallelogram is also	
1	a rectangle.
2	a rhombus.
3	a quadrilateral.
4	a trapezoid.

E No prime number	
1	is greater than 11.
2	is even.
3	has a composite factor.
4	is between 15 and 20.

F No triangle has	
1	three congruent angles.
2	two right angles.
3	an obtuse angle.
4	two acute angles.

Make up a generalization.
Challenge a partner to decide if your generalization is true or false.

Put 1 2 3 4 in a bag.

For Each Round

Choose A, B, C, D, E, or F.

Pick a tile. Pick two tiles if your group has only two students.

Determine whether the words next to your tile number complete the sentence to make a true statement or a false statement.

Discuss: Which three endings make the sentence true? Why?

Decide: Which ending makes the sentence false? Why?

A All triangles have	
1	**three angles.**
2	**two congruent sides.**
3	**the measures of the interior angles totaling 180°.**
4	**three vertices.**

B All even numbers have	
1	**an even factor.**
2	**at least one odd factor.**
3	**at least two prime factors.**
4	**more than one factor.**

C All quadrilaterals have	
1	**two diagonals.**
2	**the measures of the interior angles totaling 360°.**
3	**at least two parallel sides.**
4	**one angle of 90° or more.**

D All isosceles triangles have	
1	**two congruent sides.**
2	**two congruent angles.**
3	**the measures of the interior angles totaling 180°.**
4	**three acute angles.**

E All odd composite numbers have	
1	**more than two factors.**
2	**at least two different prime factors.**
3	**only odd factors.**
4	**an odd prime factor.**

F All trapezoids have	
1	**two congruent diagonals.**
2	**two non-parallel sides.**
3	**two non-congruent angles.**
4	**the measures of the interior angles totaling 360°.**

If you have more time Make up a generalization.
Challenge a partner to decide if your generalization is true or false.

Teamwork

Get 0 1 2 3 4 5 6 7 8 9
and 0 1 2 3 4 5 6 7 8 9.

Repeat for Each Round

Take turns doing the steps listed below in order.
Change steps when a new round begins.

STEP 1 **Choose a point on the grid and display its ordered pair. Explain.**

STEP 2 **Find a point on the grid that is on the same vertical line as the first point and display its ordered pair. Explain the pattern.**

STEP 3 **Find a point on the grid that is on the same horizontal line as the first point and display its ordered pair. Explain the pattern.**

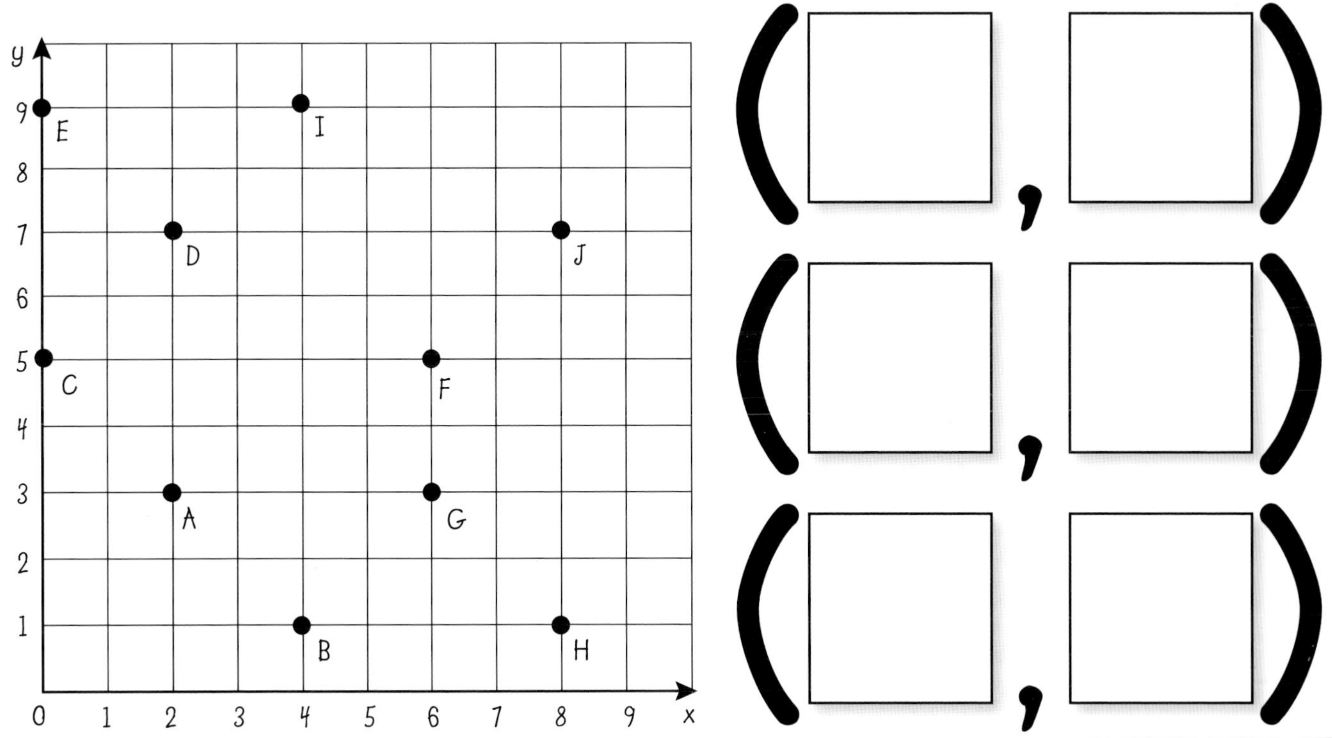

Choose a new point on the grid. Repeat the steps for your point.

Teamwork

Get 0 1 2 3 4 5 6 7 8 9 and 0 1 2 3 4 5 6 7 8 9.

Repeat for Each Round Take turns doing the steps listed below in order. Change steps when a new round begins.

STEP 1 **Choose a point on the grid and display its ordered pair.**

STEP 2 **Display the ordered pair for a point that is on the same horizontal line as the first point. Explain why the point you chose is correct.**

STEP 3 **Display the ordered pair for a point that is on the same vertical line as the first point. Explain why the point you chose is correct.**

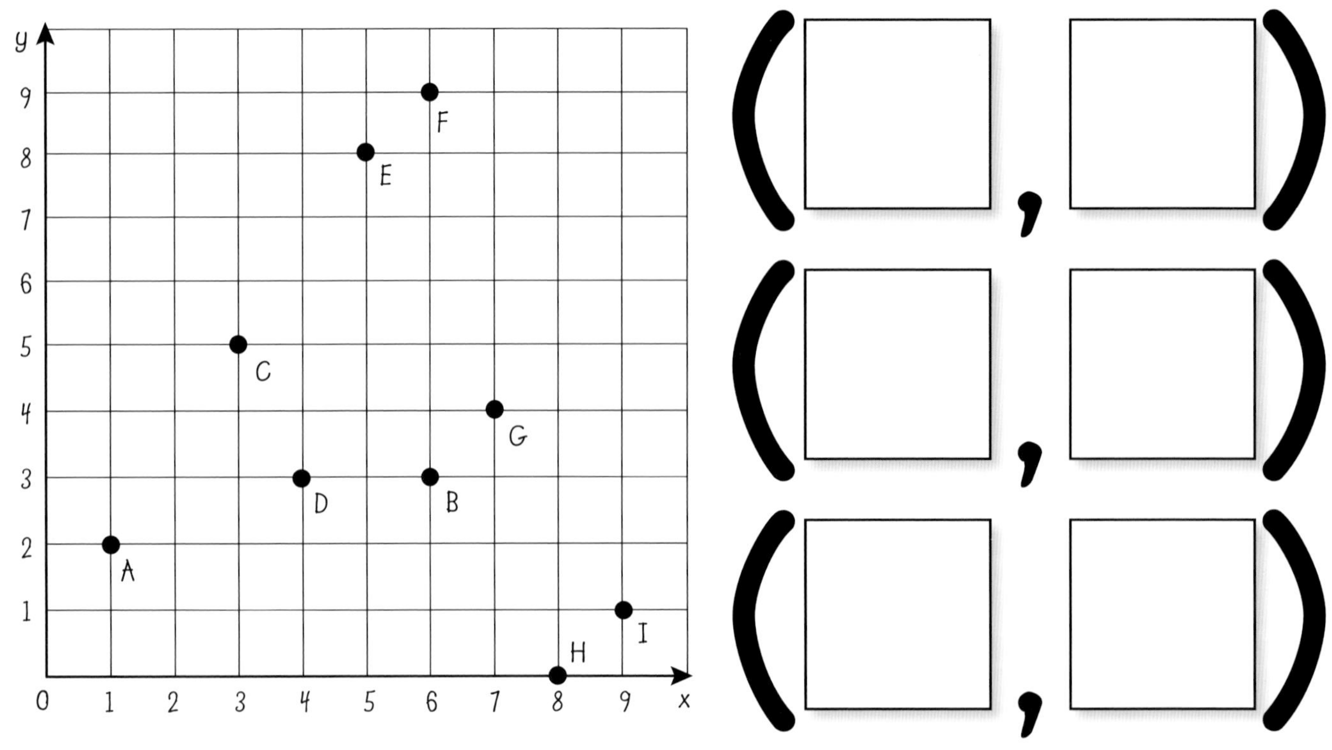

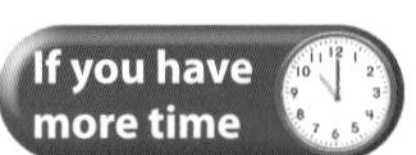

Choose a new point on the grid. Repeat the steps for your point.

Display the Digits

0 1 2 3 4 5 6 7 8 9

Read the two ordered pairs. Tell whether the line segment connecting the two points is a horizontal or a vertical line segment. Calculate the length of that line segment. Display each 0–9 tile exactly once. If you have a partner, take turns.

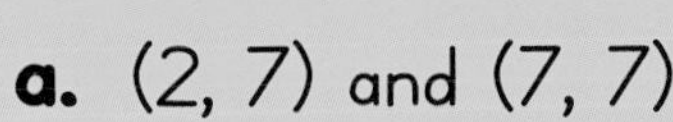

a. (2, 7) and (7, 7) 

b. (0, 7) and (0, 14) 

c. (3, 2) and (3, 10) 

d. (1, 5) and (4, 5) 

e. (1, 3) and (1, 12) 

f. (6, 0) and (6, 6) 

g. (7, 5) and (11, 5) 

h. (0, 0) and (1, 0) 

i. (1, 2) and (1, 22) 

Make up another puzzle like this one.
Ask your partner to display the answers with 0–9 tiles.

Display the Digits

0 1 2 3 4 5 6 7 8 9

Pick a tile. That is the length of a line segment.
Find the two ordered pairs that determine the endpoints of a horizontal or a vertical line segment that has that length.
Display each 0–9 tile exactly once. If you have a partner, take turns.

a. (0, 0) and (0, 1)

b. (2, 6) and (8, 6)

c. (2, 4) and (6, 4)

d. (5, 3) and (5, 5)

e. (3, 1) and (11, 1)

f. (10, 12) and (10, 15)

g. (7, 3) and (7, 10)

h. (2, 3) and (2, 3)

i. (0, 5) and (0, 14)

j. (6, 7) and (11, 7)

a	b	c	d	e
f	g	h	i	j

Make up another puzzle like this one.
Ask your partner to display the answers with 0–9 tiles.

Solve the simpler problem on the left. Use that solution to help you solve the problem on the right. Display each 0–9 tile exactly once. If you have a partner, take turns.

There are 7 rows of canned beans in a display case. In the first row there are 2 cans. In the second row there are 3 cans. In the third row there are 4 cans. How many cans are in the 7th row?

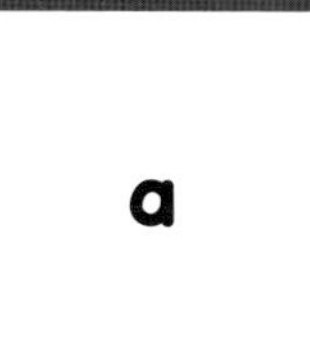

How many cans are there in all 7 rows?

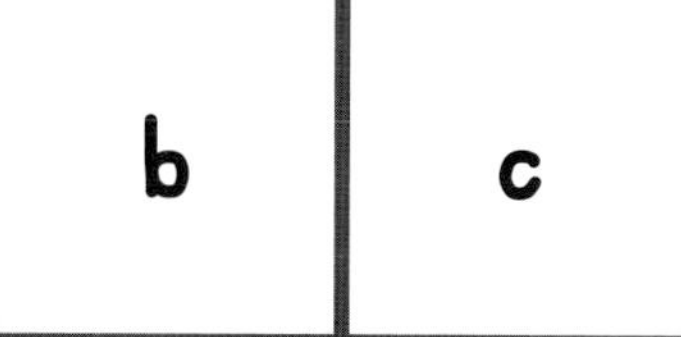

A store owner cuts a rope into 5 equal pieces to make a display. How many cuts does he make?

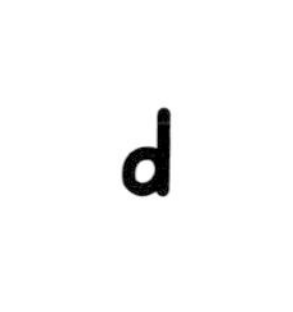

How many cuts are made if the owner cuts another rope into 18 equal pieces?

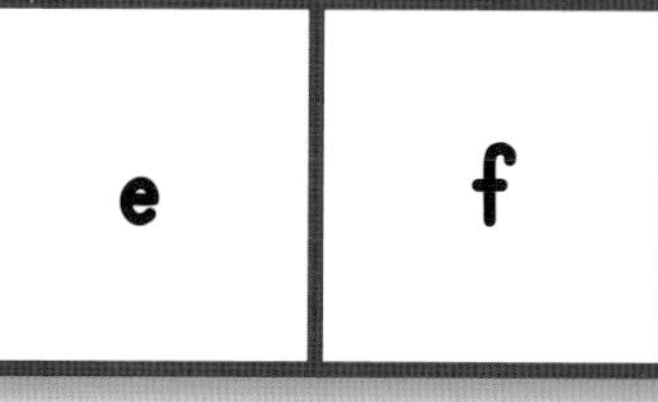

There are 3 cans of beans in the first row of a display case. The second row has 6 cans. The store owner adds 3 more cans every time he makes another row. How many cans are in the third row?

9

How many cans of beans are there in the 23rd row?

Martha has 2 blouses and 2 skirts. How many different outfits can she make?

4

Her sister has 4 blouses and 5 skirts. How many outfits can her sister make?

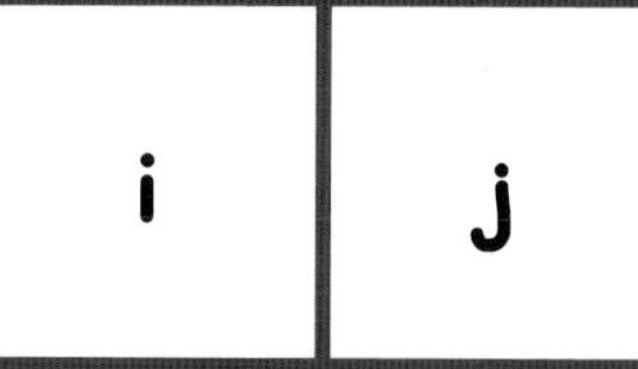

Make up another problem like this one. Ask your partner to solve your problem.

Answer the question by solving a simpler problem.
Display each 0–9 tile exactly once.
If you have a partner, take turns.

Betty is designing a banner. She needs to cut a piece of yarn into 48 equal pieces. How many cuts does she need to make?

a	b

Hank has 7 trousers and 5 dress shirts. How many different outfits can he make?

c	d

Gina draws a pattern of dots. The first picture has 3 dots, the second picture has 6 dots, the third picture has 10 dots, and the fourth picture has 15 dots. How many dots are in the sixth picture?

e	f

Sal's Pizza Parlor sells 4 sizes of pizza (individual, small, medium, and large), 10 different toppings possible, and 4 different crust styles. How many different pizzas can you choose if you order one size, one topping, and one crust?

g	h	i

Hakeem collects baseball cards in an album. He puts a different number of cards on each page. On the first page, he puts 2 cards. On the second page, he puts 3 cards. On the third page, he puts 4 cards. On which page will there be 10 cards?

j

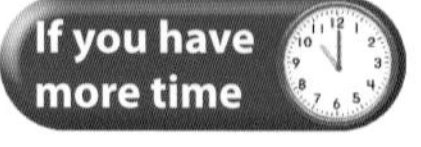

Make up another problem like one of these.
Ask your partner to solve your problem.

Teamwork

Get paper and a pencil, a ruler, and coordinate grid paper.
Put 1 2 3 4 in a bag.

Repeat for Each Round

Choose **a**, **b**, **c**, **d**, **e**, or **f**.
Pick a tile. Pick two tiles if your group has only two students.
Do the jobs listed below in order.
To find your job, find the number that matches the tile you chose.

 **Read the equation, and the values given for *x*.**

 **Make a table of values for *x* and *y*.**

 **Plot a point on the grid paper for each ordered pair from the table of values.**

 **Connect the points to graph the equation.**

a. $y = x + 1$
Let $x = 0, 1, 2, 3$

b. $y = 3x$
Let $x = 0, 1, 2, 3$

c. $y = x - 2$
Let $x = 2, 3, 4, 5$

d. $y = x + 5$
Let $x = 0, 2, 4, 5$

e. $y = 4x$
Let $x = 0, 1, 2, 3$

f. $y = x - 3$
Let $x = 3, 4, 5, 6$

Make up an equation. Choose values for *x*. Follow steps 1–4 for your equation. Use the values of *x* that you chose.

Teamwork

Get Started or

Get paper and a pencil, a ruler, and coordinate grid paper.
Put 1 2 3 4 in a bag.

Repeat for Each Round

Choose **a**, **b**, or **c**.
Pick a tile. Pick two tiles if your group has only two students.
Do the jobs listed below in order.
To find your job, find the number that matches the tile you chose.

1 **Plot the three ordered pairs on grid paper.**

2 **Connect the points. Extend the line.**

3 **Copy and complete the table. Explain the pattern.**

4 **Find the linear equation for the straight line.**

a. Plot and label these points:
E (2, 6), F (4, 8), G (6, 10)

x	y
2	
4	
6	
8	
10	

$y =$ ___

b. Plot and label these points:
H (1, 3), I (2, 6), J (3, 9)

x	y
0	
1	
2	
3	
4	

$y =$ ___

c. Plot and label these points:
K (3, 4), L (4, 5), M (6, 7)

x	y
0	
3	
4	
5	
6	

$y =$ ___

Name four other points that would be on one of these lines.
Repeat for each of the other two lines.

Display the Digits

0 1 2 3 4 5 6 7 8 9

Choose a table. Explain how to complete each row. Say the ordered pairs for that equation. Repeat for the other table. Display each 0–9 tile exactly once. If you have a partner, take turns.

x	$y = 2x + 4$	y
0	$y = 2(0) + 4$	a
1	$y = 2(1) + 4$	b
2	$y = 2($ c $) + 4$	d
3	$y = 2(3) + 4$	1 e
4	$y = 2(4) + 4$	12

x	$y = 6x - 2$	y
1	$y = 6(1) - 2$	4
3	$y = 6($ f $) - 2$	g 6
h	$y = 6(5) - 2$	28
7	$y = 6($ i $) - 2$	40
j	$y = 6(9) - 2$	52

a	b	c	d	e
f	g	h	i	j

Find five other ordered pairs on the graph of each equation. If you have more time, make up a puzzle like one of these. Ask a partner to solve your puzzle.

Display the Digits

0 1 2 3 4 5 6 7 8 9

Say each equation. Describe a rule in words. Complete the ordered pair so that it can be used to locate a point on the graph. Display each 0–9 tile exactly once. If you have a partner, take turns.

$y = 5x - 1$ (4, [a][b])

$y = 7x + 4$ (3, [c][d])

$y = x \div 4$ (120, [e][f])

$y = 2x + 2$ ([g][h], 94)

$y = 3x - 13$ ([i], [j])

(Hint: Complete this one last!)

Make up another puzzle like one of these.
Ask your partner to display the missing coordinates with 0–9 tiles.

Teamwork

Get Started Put 1 2 3 4 in a bag.

Repeat for Each Round Choose **a, b, c, d,** or **e**. Pick a tile. Pick two tiles if your group has only two students. Do the jobs listed below in order. To find your job, find the number that matches the tile you chose.

1. **Read the problem. Tell your team what you know and what you need to find.**
2. **Determine the "end" of the problem. Explain why working backward is a good strategy.**
3. **Explain how to solve the problem by working backward. Use mental math.**
4. **Check your answer. Make sure it is correct. How do you know? Explain.**

a. The Eagles scored 15 points during a soccer game. During the 4th quarter, they scored 4 points. They scored 3 points during the 3rd quarter. They scored an equal number of points in the 1st and 2nd quarters. How many points did they score in those quarters?

b. Marina spent $105.50 on three new items of clothing. Tax was $5.50. A pair of jeans cost $45.00, and a sweater cost $27.50. How much did her blouse cost?

c. T.J. arrived at school at 7:30 A.M. It took him 35 minutes to get to school, 25 minutes to eat, and 20 minutes to get dressed. What time did T.J. get up this morning?

d. The chess club sponsored an event to raise money. They used $400 to host a chess tournament. This was $\frac{1}{3}$ of the money raised. How much money did the club raise?

e. Stefan used $25 from his bank account to buy baseball cards, $10 to buy his sister's birthday gift, and $5 to bring to school for a class party. His bank account balance is now $72. How much money did Stefan have in his bank account before he paid for these things?

If you have more time Create more problems that can be solved by working backward. Repeat steps 1 – 4 for your problems.

Teamwork

Get a pencil and some grid paper to represent a coordinate plane. Put 1 2 3 4 in a bag.

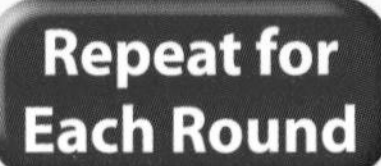

Choose **a, b, c,** or **d**. Pick a tile. Pick two tiles if your group has only two students. Do the jobs listed below in order. To find your job, find the number that matches the tile you chose.

Read the problem. Tell your team what you know and what you need to find.

Suggest one possible answer to the problem.

Check your answer to make sure it is correct. Explain how you know.

Suggest another possible answer to the problem. Explain how you got it.

a. The ending position on a coordinate plane is (3, 6). The starting position is (1, 3). What steps could you use to work backward from the ending position to the starting position?

b. The Cougars scored 8 points in their recent soccer game. During the 4th quarter, they scored 1 point. During the 3rd quarter, they also scored 1 point. During the 1st and 2nd quarters, the number of points scored in each quarter was an even number. What did the Cougars score in the first quarter?

c. Bethany drew a quadrilateral. After looking at her picture, she decided to cut off two indentical triangles with a pair of scissors. Her final shape was a parallelogram. What shapes could Bethany originally have drawn?

d. The ending position on a coordinate plane is (12, 5). The starting position is (9, 1). What steps could you use to work backward from the ending position to the starting position?

Create more problems that can be solved on grid paper by working backward. Repeat steps 1 – 4 for your problems.

